THE MAKING OF AMERICA

STUDY GUIDE

A Course Prepared by
The National Center for Constitutional Studies

Contents

Preface

In the great formative period of the United States two centuries ago, the American Founding Fathers became acutely aware that all mankind is seeking the same three things:

1. Freedom
2. Prosperity
3. Peace

They set out to find a system of government that would provide these things for the people of America. Unfortunately, in their own day no such government existed. They therefore determined to sit down and invent one.

This is their story.

As we shall see, the search for the "ancient principles" of sound government was a prolonged and painful one. What was worse, when they finally discovered what these principles were, it was difficult to persuade many people to accept them. Getting people to assume the responsibilities of freedom and self-government was one of the most discouraging parts of their political adventure.

So the structuring of the American success formula for freedom, prosperity, and peace was a hard-won achievement. Nevertheless, it did finally produce in America the first free people in modern times.

That is why this course is important. The Founders laid the foundation for us. We must preserve it. To do so, we have to know what their success formula consisted of. It is all set forth in our textbook entitled *The Making of America*. This accompanying study guide is designed to provide you with an easily understood overview of the great principles of America's freedom and the stirring history of their discovery and adoption.

Throughout this study guide you will find occasional blanks. The purpose of these blanks is to encourage concentration on each of the important points being discussed in the lesson. Each missing word will be furnished to you by the instructor during the discussion of each lesson. In case you miss one of the words, you will find it listed on pages 133–138.

Left: *The Centennial celebration of the Declaration of Independence at Independence Hall, Philadelphia, July 4, 1876.*

What is the
National Center for Constitutional Studies?

The National Center for Constitutional Studies is a nonprofit educational foundation created to teach the U.S. Constitution in the tradition of America's Founding Fathers. Founded in 1971 by Dr. W. Cleon Skousen, NCCS has taught thousands of families throughout America the original principles and ideas drafted by our Founding Fathers over 230 years ago.

Our purpose is to help build the dynamic culture of liberty and union which the Founders sought to secure for themselves and their posterity. We gratefully acknowledge, as they did, that America and its Constitution were established by the hand of God; and thus we advocate morality and religious principles as the essential foundation of human happiness and freedom.

In the final years of his life, Thomas Jefferson called upon the American people to "preserve inviolate [the] Constitution, which [if] cherished in all its chastity and purity, will prove in the end a blessing to all the nations of the earth." We believe that as we learn and implement the sound principles taught by our Founding Fathers, America's divine stewardship as a beacon of liberty to all mankind will yet be fulfilled.

Our program is a positive, constructive campaign of education to help our country get back on its constitutional track. Funding for our work is provided by donations from modern-day patriots who are dedicated to strengthening America by spreading the message of freedom. All contributions to NCCS are tax-deductible under Internal Revenue Code section 501[c] (3).

In addition to its popular constitutional seminars, NCCS produces and distributes books, newsletters, CDs, DVDs and other educational materials for adults and children. For further information please contact:

National Center for Constitutional Studies
37777 West Juniper Road
Malta, Idaho 83342

(800) 388-4512 (Product orders only)
(208) 645-2625
(208) 645-2667 (Fax)

www.nccs.net
Seminar Information: www.nccs.net/seminars

1

I

Introduction: The Making of America

In order to appreciate the historical setting of the making of America, we need to review some of the little-known or forgotten events that led to the discovery and development of the Western Hemisphere. The Founding Fathers would probably consider this one of the most important parts of our study, because it covers the tempestuous historical period that gave birth to our great American heritage.

Since the discovery of America nearly 500 years ago, some rather amazing things have happened. For example:

A. Man has explored and mapped the entire planet earth including the land that lies under the ___Seas___.

B. We have gone through six great leaps in human progress:

1. The Industrial Revolution, which transformed many basic industries (iron, textiles, shoe manufacturing, shipbuilding, etc.) and made consumer goods abundant and inexpensive.

2. The Machine Revolution, which transferred much arduous labor from muscle power to machine power, allowing man to turn his energies to a wider range of endeavors.

Hand loom, used before 1785.

Arkwright's first spinning frame.

3. The Transportation Revolution, which made the world a community of nations.

4. The Communications Revolution, which made the people of the world a community of neighbors.

5. The Energy Development Revolution, which improved the standard of living all over the world.

6. The phenomenal Computer Revolution, which enables machines to "think" and perform an astonishing array of functions.

C. All of these were made possible by the Freedom Revolution. Freedom became the ___Key___ to genuine human progress in all areas—food, medicine, disease control, creature comforts, and many more.

II

Each generation must study the lessons of history so that ___mistakes___ of the past will not be repeated. American history begins with the discovery of a gigantic continent in the midst of the western sea.

A. In the past, many American history books said that Columbus was the first person to prove the world was ___round___.

B. This led Professor Samuel Eliot Morison of Harvard to write: "Of all the vulgar errors connected with Columbus, the most persistent and the most absurd is that he had to convince people 'the world was round.' Every educated man in his day believed the world to be a ___sphere___, [and] every European university so taught geography." (Samuel Eliot Morison, *Admiral of the Ocean Sea*, Boston: Little, Brown and Company, 1942, p. 33.)

C. Then how did such a story get started? For several generations our history books told how Columbus could not get support for his project until he convinced the royal court that the earth was round. Dr. Morison, calling this story "pure ___moonshine___," wrote: "Washington Irving, scenting his opportunity for a picturesque and moving scene, took a fictitious account of this nonexistent [incident] published 130 years after the event, elaborated on it, and let his imagination go completely." (Ibid., p. 89.) It is such a good story that it has been difficult to get it out of the history books.

Three centuries of Crusades introduced West to East.

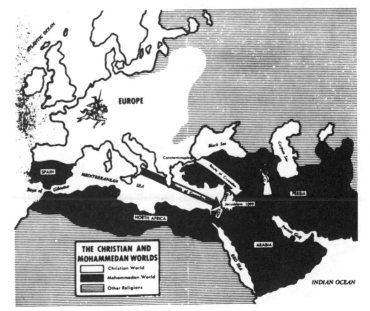

THE CHRISTIAN AND MOHAMMEDAN WORLDS

Christian World
Mohammedan World
Other Religions

How the Crusades led to the discovery of America.   **III**

A. The Crusades began around A.D. 1100 and were undertaken to liberate the Holy Land from the Muslims. The Crusaders pursued this goal for approximately 300 years but eventually __failed__.

B. Nevertheless, contact with the Mediterranean peoples, especially the Arabs, introduced Europeans to the luxuries of the Far East:

     1. Spices

     2. Rugs and tapestries

     3. Jewelry and perfumes

     4. Beautiful fabrics made of silk

C. At first the Europeans purchased these luxuries through the __Arab__ merchants who controlled the trade routes by both land and sea. However, the kings of Europe thought it would be cheaper to make contact with China and Indonesia directly.

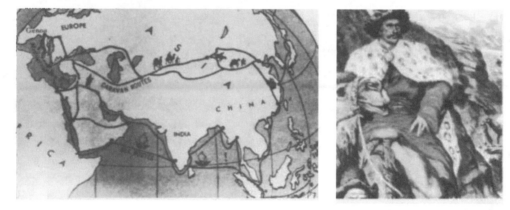

Marco Polo's journey made Europeans aware of the riches of the East.

D. Marco Polo accompanied his father and uncle to China in A.D. 1271. He was only 17 when he left and did not return for __20__ years. His description of the fabulous riches of China made many Europeans anxious to establish trade routes to the Far East either by land or by sea.

Prior to Columbus, the Portuguese and English tried to reach the Far East by going __west__ across the Atlantic.   **IV**

A. As we have already noted, European scholars knew the earth was round, and the temptation to reach China by sailing west across the Atlantic was seriously considered. However, the Greek geographer Eratosthenes had estimated around 200 B.C. that the circumference of the earth was __27,750__ miles. (Bjorn Landstrom, *Columbus*, New York: The Macmillan Co., 1966, p. 9.) If that was the case, they felt, China could be reached only by "island hopping." The Portuguese were encouraged when they discovered the Azores in 1439, and by 1452 they had reached the mid-Atlantic islands of Flores and Corvo, located 1,000 miles from Newfoundland. However, at this latitude the Portuguese were constantly fighting winds that were blowing _eastward_____, so they finally gave up and focused their efforts on reaching the Far East by going around Africa. (Morison, *Admiral of the Ocean Sea*, p. 59.)

B. Meanwhile, in 1484, a group of wealthy merchants in England employed an Italian sea captain, Giovanni Cabota, to sail out into the Atlantic in search of islands which could be stepping-stones to China. He soon returned with the report that he hadn't found any islands. Had he continued, he would have discovered America eight years before Columbus.

V. Columbus makes his great discovery.

A. In 1474, an Italian geographer named Paulo Toscanelli prepared a map showing that the distance between Spain and China was probably no more than __3000_____ miles. (It was closer to 13,000 miles!) Shortly after this, Columbus began working on a map of his own and reduced the distance even more. (Landstrom, *Columbus*, pp. 30-31.)

B. In mapping his strategy, Columbus put great store in reaching an island which Marco Polo had called Cipangu but which we call _Japan_____. Marco Polo said he had never been there but he understood it was about 1,500 miles east of China and fabulously rich in pearls, gold, and silks.

Paulo Toscanelli

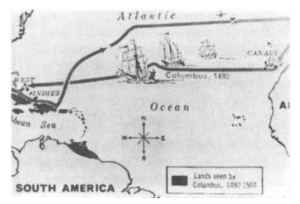

C. Columbus studied Marco Polo's work carefully and decided that Cipangu was farther south than the maps indicated. He therefore launched his voyage from the Canary Islands, located just off the coast of Africa. This was fortunate because the winds at this latitude blow _westward_____. Columbus had extremely favorable weather and arrived in the Bahamas at what is believed to be San Salvador or Watlings Island, October 12, 1492.

VI. The Spanish soon undertook to conquer the entire Western Hemisphere.

A. Using the large island just east of Cuba (now called Haiti and the Dominican Republic, but called _Hispaniola_____ by Columbus), the Spanish set up their headquarters and prepared to establish their claims to the entire continents of North and South America.

B. In 1519, Hernando Cortez took a few hundred Spanish soldiers and conquered several million ___Aztecs___ and their allies in Mexico, where there were fabulous quantities of gold and silver.

Hernando Cortez

Francisco Pizarro

C. In 1531, Francisco Pizarro, who was 61 years of age, launched a campaign in Peru and conquered several million Indians who were called ___Incas___. Once again the Spanish gained great treasures in gold and silver.

D. The Spanish then moved north into what is now the United States. Juan Ponce de Leon discovered Florida. Hernando de Soto discovered the Mississippi. Francisco de Coronado explored the Southwest, and his men discovered the Grand Canyon.

E. It was obviously just a question of time until the Spanish would occupy the entire Western Hemisphere. In the process, they established a very harsh colonial administration under ___Rulers___ Law, which means that all power is vested in the ruler.

F. Suddenly, however, the steady march of Spanish conquest to the north came to a halt, and the Spanish were displaced by the ___French___ in the aggressive colonization of North America.

How the French blunted the northern expansion of Spain.

A. Just as the 1500s belonged to the Spanish, the 1600s belonged to the French. They first began exploring North America as early as 1524.

B. In 1534, Jacques Cartier was searching for a passage to the Pacific and discovered the St. Lawrence River. He sailed as far as he could but was stopped at Chino Falls. A city was later built near this place and named ___Montreal___.

C. In 1659, two French explorers discovered the headwaters of the Mississippi River, and in 1678, Cavelier de la Salle traveled down the full length of the river to the Gulf of Mexico. In 1718 the French founded ___New Orleans___ at the mouth of the Mississippi River.

D. The French established ___80,000___ settlers along the waterways that

VII

Cavelier de la Salle

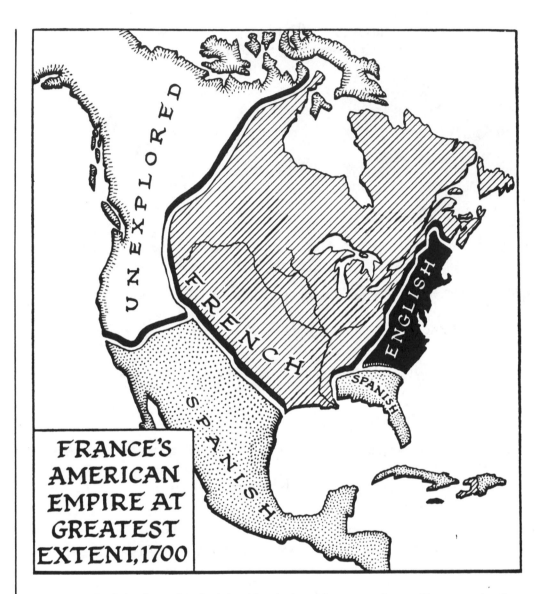

FRANCE'S
AMERICAN
EMPIRE AT
GREATEST
EXTENT, 1700

controlled the heartland of the North American continent. Fortunately, the Spanish were far too busy collecting gold and silver in Mexico and South America to press their claims very vigorously in North America.

E. The French had no form of representative government, but ran their affairs under a type of Ruler's Law very much like the Spanish system. Nevertheless, they created an impasse with the Spanish which allowed the English to settle nearly ___3,000,000___ colonists on the Atlantic seaboard by 1776 and introduce the fundamentals for a representative form of government which we call ___Peoples___ Law.

VIII As the early colonists came to America, they brought a great gift from England.

A. The English were just about the only Europeans who fought to preserve the basic institutes of the ___Anglo - Saxon___ culture under People's Law.

[handwritten: Roman's coincidentally coming]

Hengist and Horsa, two Saxon chiefs, introduced these principles in Britain around A.D. 450. Unfortunately, after 600 years under People's Law, the people of England nearly lost their freedom entirely.

B. The conquest of England in 1066 by the Normans brought elements of feudal law, Roman civil law, and canon law to England. All of these included elements of Ruler's Law which <u>corrupted</u> the Anglo-Saxon system.

C. Thomas Jefferson describes how the Normans introduced feudalism and Ruler's Law in England:

> Our Saxon ancestors held their lands, as they did their personal property, in absolute dominion, disincumbered.... William the Norman [Conqueror] first introduced that system [of feudalism]. The lands which had belonged to those who fell in the battle of Hastings, and in the subsequent insurrections of his reign, formed a considerable proportion of the lands of the whole kingdom. These he granted out, subject to feudal duties, as he did also those of a great number of his new [English] subjects, who, by persuasions or threats, were induced to surrender them for that purpose.... A general principle was introduced, that 'all lands in England were held either mediately or immediately by the Crown.' (Saul K. Padover, *The Complete Jefferson*, New York: Tudor Publishing Co., 1943, pp. 16–17.)

William the Conquerer

[handwritten: AGINCORT ?]

D. By 1215, the oppressive policies of the Normans had become intolerable even to those who had supported the Normans. Therefore, the English barons rebelled against King John and compelled him to sign the famous <u>Magna Carta</u>, in which they itemized their rights.

E. Ever since then, each generation has had to fight to maintain these rights. In fact, there were periods in English history when the rights of the people were almost completely suppressed in spite of the Magna Charta. However, the barons, church leaders, knights, and burgesses finally gained enough influence to require the king to let them represent the people in a primitive English <u>Parliament</u>. There they were able to force the king to recognize many of their basic rights and gradually limit his power. Parliament was actually an expansion of the king's council and first appeared as a parliamentary forum in 1264.

F. Early in the 1600s, Sir Edward Coke, an English judge, found himself doing things to Englishmen that violated their traditional rights. He repented and launched a campaign to revive interest in the specific rights set forth in the Magna Charta which he said not only belonged to the barons, knights, and burgesses, but to all <u>free men</u>.

G. By 1628 the abuses of Charles I were so harsh that Parliament forced him to sign a famous document called the <u>Petition of Rights</u>. Later, however, he ignored his commitments, and Parliament seized power and turned control of the government over to Oliver Cromwell. Charles I was convicted of treason and beheaded.

H. In 1660, Parliament put Charles II on the throne, and after he died in 1685, his brother was allowed to ascend the throne as James II. However, James II was so ruthless that Parliament dethroned him in 1688 in what is called the "Glorious Revolution." Parliament then entered into an agreement with his daughter and her husband (William and Mary) to take over the throne

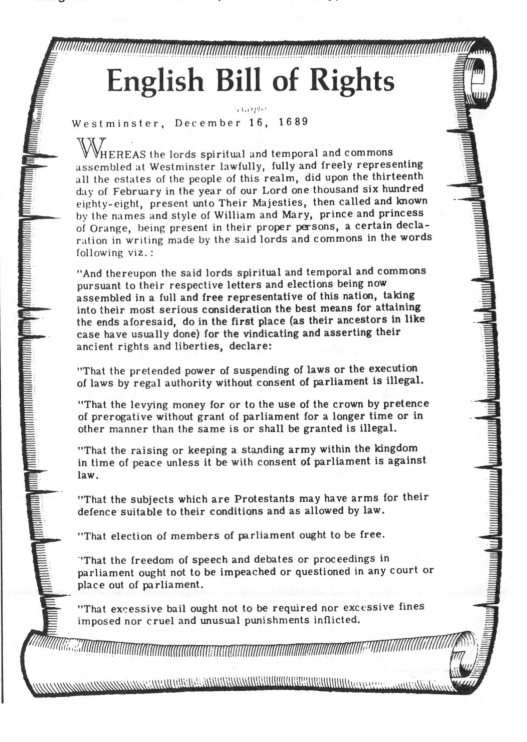

English Bill of Rights

Westminster, December 16, 1689

WHEREAS the lords spiritual and temporal and commons assembled at Westminster lawfully, fully and freely representing all the estates of the people of this realm, did upon the thirteenth day of February in the year of our Lord one thousand six hundred eighty-eight, present unto Their Majesties, then called and known by the names and style of William and Mary, prince and princess of Orange, being present in their proper persons, a certain declaration in writing made by the said lords and commons in the words following viz. :

"And thereupon the said lords spiritual and temporal and commons pursuant to their respective letters and elections being now assembled in a full and free representative of this nation, taking into their most serious consideration the best means for attaining the ends aforesaid, do in the first place (as their ancestors in like case have usually done) for the vindicating and asserting their ancient rights and liberties, declare:

"That the pretended power of suspending of laws or the execution of laws by regal authority without consent of parliament is illegal.

"That the levying money for or to the use of the crown by pretence of prerogative without grant of parliament for a longer time or in other manner than the same is or shall be granted is illegal.

"That the raising or keeping a standing army within the kingdom in time of peace unless it be with consent of parliament is against law.

"That the subjects which are Protestants may have arms for their defence suitable to their conditions and as allowed by law.

"That election of members of parliament ought to be free.

"That the freedom of speech and debates or proceedings in parliament ought not to be impeached or questioned in any court or place out of parliament.

"That excessive bail ought not to be required nor excessive fines imposed nor cruel and unusual punishments inflicted.

providing they would sign an English _Bill_ _of_ _Rights_ . This document was signed in 1689.

I. All of these hard-won rights of the English became part of the American heritage. Americans owe a great debt of gratitude to the tens of thousands of Englishmen who were imprisoned, hanged, beheaded, tortured, burned at the stake, or forced into exile as they tried to reestablish those inalienable rights which many Americans in our day casually take for granted.

The English begin the development of Peoples' Law in America.

IX

A. Queen Elizabeth I tried to head off Spanish colonization north of Florida by commissioning Sir Walter Raleigh to establish a colony on Roanoke Island off the coast of what is now North Carolina. The first colony established in 1585 was starved out. The second one, established in 1587, disappeared. The experiment cost Sir Walter Raleigh over $200,000.

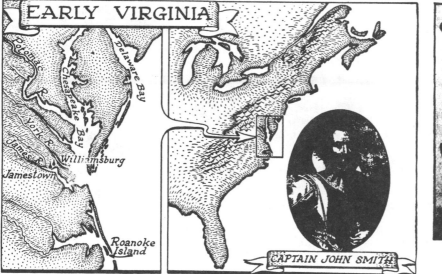

Advertising for settlers, 1609.

B. In 1607, King James I once more attempted to head off the Spanish by allowing a group of London businessmen to set up a colony in what is now Virginia. It became known as Jamestown. The businessmen thought the colony would be more profitable if it practiced secular _Commune-ism_ . The project was a failure until they divided up the land and began shifting for themselves.

C. In 1620, the same company sponsored the settlement of a group of Pilgrims in Northern Virginia, but their ship landed farther north. There they established Plymouth, in what is now Massachusetts. The patron company had given up secular communism in Virginia but still thought it would work among the Pilgrims if they practiced _Christian_ communism. As Christians, they were supposed to look upon their neighbors as "brethren" and cooperate together. However, the project failed and many starved. Governor William Bradford wrote:

> At length, after much debate...the [governor] gave way that they should set corne every man for his owne perticuler, and in that regard trust to them selves;...and so assigned to every family a parcell of land, according to the proportion of their number.

After one year under this procedure, the governor was able to write:

> This had very good success; for it made all hands very industrious, so as much more corne was planted then other waise would have bene.... The women now wente willingly into the feild, and tooke their litle-ons with them to set corne, which before would aledg weaknes, and inabilitie; whom to have compelled would have bene thought great tiranie and oppression. (William T. Davis, ed., *Bradford's History of Plymouth Plantation,* New York: Charles Scribner's Sons, 1923, p. 146.)

Pilgrims in Massachusetts escaped starvation with help from friendly Indians (left).
Puritan immigrants (right) *fled religious persecution in England and set up their own theocracy in Boston.*

D. The people who settled Plymouth were called "Separatists," or Pilgrims, because they wanted to separate themselves from the national or official Church of England. The next people to come to Massachusetts Bay, beginning in 1623, were ___Puritans___ who did not want to separate from the Church of England but to purify it. Because of bitter persecution by Charles I, thousands fled to Massachusetts, especially between 1628 and 1640. Their first center of government was Salem, then Charlestown, and finally Boston. However, they made the mistake of having their Puritan Church run the affairs of state, and they drove from their midst any with dissenting views. These included Anne Hutchinson, Roger Williams, and Thomas Hooker, all of whom moved south to create new settlements in what became Connecticut and Rhode Island. Since they could not bear the arbitrary kind of theocratic government instituted in Boston, the question was, "How do we set up a strong and just government?"

Emigration to the Connecticut Valley, 1636.

E. The man who found the answer was Reverend Thomas ___Hooker___.
One hundred and five years before Thomas Jefferson was born (1638),
Reverend Hooker gave a sermon announcing that he had discovered in the
history of ancient Israel the principles of government which would be fair
and just. The villages of Connecticut therefore banded together in 1639 and
adopted a constitution (written largely by Hooker) based on the principles
found in the first chapter of Deuteronomy. Rhode Islanders then copied this
constitution, and these two colonies had one of the most satisfactory
systems of government during the entire colonial period. Reverend
Hooker's constitution for Connecticut was the first ___written___
constitution in America. ___= The Fundamental Orders of Connecticut___ "

The English colonists came to America with a sense of "Divine ___Mission___"
or "Manifest Destiny."   **X**

A. Professor Conrad Cherry said, "The belief that America had been
providentially chosen for a special ___destiny___ has deep roots in
the American past." (Conrad Cherry, *God's New Israel,* Englewood Cliffs,
N.J.: Prentice-Hall, 1971, p. 1.)

B. ___Geographically___, the Founders felt their commonwealth of
freedom would eventually cover the whole North American continent.
(Ibid., pp. 111, 129; see also Albert Weinberg, *Manifest Destiny,* Baltimore:
The Johns Hopkins Press, 1935, pp. 1-2, 43.)

C. As far as ___population___ was concerned, John Adams said they were
building a Constitution and a system of government which would one day
serve a population of between "200 and 300 million freemen." (Quoted in
Adrienne Koch, ed., *The American Enlightenment,* New York: G. Braziller,
1965, p. 131.)

D. The Founders did not consider themselves a master race but master
___servants___ who had an obligation to their Creator to design a system
which would benefit the whole world. As John Adams said:

   I always consider the settlement of America with reverence and

John Adams

wonder, as the opening of a grand scene and design in Providence for the illumination of the ignorant, and the emancipation of the slavish part of mankind all over the earth. (Quoted in Ernest Lee Tuveson, *Redeemer Nation,* Chicago: The University of Chicago Press, 1974, p. 25.)

XI

How the split developed between England and her American colonies.

A. When George III took over the throne of England, he was very popular. Here is why:

1. Around 1700, Parliament suddenly realized that all the immediate heirs to the English throne were sympathetic both in religion and politics with the king of ___France___. Therefore, the Settlement Act of 1701 ordered that no person could become ruler of England in the future unless he or she had descended through a granddaughter of James I named Sophia. Sophia had married the Elector of Hanover, Germany.

2. Queen Anne died in 1714. Therefore, George I, Elector of Hanover, became king of England even though he was a ___German___.

3. George II, another German, became king in 1727. He ruled so long (until 1760) that even his crown prince died.

4. George III, the grandson of George II, was the first king of that century who was not a ___German___. He was born in England, educated in England, spoke English beautifully, and considered himself a "patriot king." He was extremely popular among the English people, but his policies began to antagonize the American colonists.

B. In the early 1760s, King George III ordered a strict enforcement of the Navigation Acts in order to suppress the purchase of foreign goods. The idea was to "buy English and keep our money at home."

C. This resulted in extensive smuggling, both in England and America. To suppress smuggling, the king authorized the prosecution of offenders in the admiralty courts, which had no ___juries___.

D. The admiralty courts issued "writs of assistance," which allowed officers to search any home or private business looking for smuggled goods.

E. Then an act in 1763 forbade the colonists to cross the mountains and settle in the ___Ohio___ ___Valley___, where some had already become established. The colonists defied this act and resentment grew.

F. In 1765, the king had his agents in Parliament pass the ___Stamp___ Act. The colonists declared this to be "taxation without representation."

It was during Parliamentary debate on the repeal of the Stamp Act that Charles Townshend asked, "Will these Americans, children planted by our care, nourished up by our indulgence . . . will they grudge to contribute their mite?" Whereupon Isaac Barre replied, "*They* planted by *your* care? No! Your oppressions planted them in America. They fled from your

King George III

tyranny.... *They* nourished up by *your* indulgence? They grew up by your neglect of them. As soon as you began to care about them, that care was exercised in sending persons to rule over them.... *They* protected by *your* arms! They have nobly taken up arms in *your* defense." (Stewart Beach, *Samuel Adams: The Fateful Years, 1774-1776*, New York: Dodd, Mead & Company, 1965, p. 69.) It was this same Isaac Barre who referred to Americans as "Sons of Liberty," a title that was immediately adopted by Sam Adams and other leaders of the resistance movement as their official name.

Revenue stamps used in 1765.

G. Although the Stamp Act was repealed in 1766, the Townshend Acts were passed in 1767. Regiments of British troops began arriving in America to enforce the collection of taxes under this new act.

H. The king even had a "____Quartering____ act" passed, which required the colonies to provide room and board for the soldiers free of charge.

I. Here are the events which finally led to the eruption of violence in America:

1. On March 5, 1770, the Boston ____Massacre____ occurred. However, when John Adams and Josiah Quincy learned that a crowd of 300 men and boys were largely responsible for provoking this conflict, they defended the soldiers and persuaded the jury to spare their lives.

The Boston Massacre.

2. Then came King George III's scheme to trick Americans into paying a tax on tea. Americans were buying Dutch tea which was being smuggled in and sold cheaper. The king decided to undersell the Dutch tea by eliminating the English brokers, but to leave the tax attached. He didn't

think Americans would mind so long as it was ___cheaper___. Then came the surprise:

a. All of the tea ships were forced to return with their cargo to England, or (as happened in Charleston) the shipments were unloaded and stored under quarantine.

b. The exception was Boston. The people refused to let the tea be unloaded, and the governor refused to let the ships return until they were unloaded.

c. The governor figured that since the Crown could confiscate any cargo not unloaded in 20 days, he would sell the tea at auction and collect the tax after all. Sam Adams saw through the scheme and pleaded with the governor to send the ships back before there was a direct confrontation with the people. The governor refused, and on December 16, 1773, during the night of the 19th day, the "Sons of Liberty" boarded the boats and threw all of the tea into the harbor. This event is known as the Boston ___Tea___ ___Party___.

The Boston Tea Party.

d. The reaction of George III was swift and vengeful:

  (1) He closed the Boston harbor and placed the city under martial law.

  (2) He put General Thomas Gage in charge of British troops in America as the new military governor of Massachusetts.

  (3) He suspended the Charter of Massachusetts and dissolved the people's elected assemblies.

  (4) He suspended all town meetings unless approved by the new military governor.

  (5) He threatened to bring serious offenders to England for trial.

  These measures are known as the ___Intolerable___ Acts.

3. The First Continental Congress convened during September and October 1774 to forestall the outbreak of war. Nevertheless, the colonists

Deadly fire from Minutemen's muskets forced the Redcoats into a costly retreat from Lexington and Concord.

were determined to stand up for their rights by whatever means were necessary.

4. In 1775 and 1776, the Americans finally felt compelled to resort to force of arms in order to defend their rights.
   a. The British raid on _Lexington_ and _Concord_ on April 19, 1775, was intended to destroy American military supplies and punish the leaders of Massachusetts who were meeting secretly.
   b. The Green Mountain Boys from Vermont then attacked and burned the British fort at Ticonderoga on May 10, 1775.
   c. That same day the Second Continental Congress convened in Philadelphia to authorize the raising of a continental army with _George_ _Washington_ as commander in chief. Their purpose at this time was not to declare independence, but merely to protect their rights.

Washington took command of the Continental Army at Cambridge, Massachusetts.

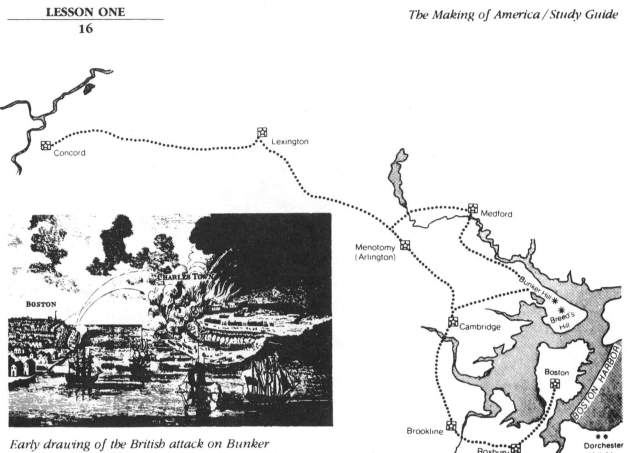

Early drawing of the British attack on Bunker Hill. During the shelling, Charlestown (now part of Boston) was destroyed by fire.

d. Meanwhile, as the American militia closed the ring around Boston, General Gage decided to attack with more than 2,000 troops. This was the Battle of Bunker Hill, which was really fought on Breed's Hill. The Americans lost around 450 men and were forced to retreat, but General Gage lost more than _____ English troops.

e. On July 3, 1775, Washington took over the siege of Boston and supreme command of the Continental Army. In October, Gage was replaced by General Sir William Howe, who had led the attack at Bunker Hill.

Conclusion

In this lesson we have covered 283 years of American history—from Columbus to the Battle of Bunker Hill. Now a new nation was about to be born.

2

The Birth of a Nation

Introduction

During a brief period of 12 months, a series of incidents changed the colonists from loyal Englishmen to loyal Americans who demanded independence from England. Here is what brought about the change.

A. During the first 15 years of King George's reign, the people met his abuses with protests and ___petitions___. However, from April 1775 to April 1776, events occurred which destroyed their feeling of loyalty and affection for the king. These events included:

1. The killing or wounding of approximately ___95___ Americans at Lexington and Concord on April 19, 1775.

2. The killing or wounding of approximately ___450___ Americans at the Battle of Bunker Hill. Of course, the British themselves lost at least 1,000 soldiers, but this did not excuse the fact that the whole conflict was a result of British oppression in the first place.

3. When some of the conservative members of Congress such as John Dickinson sent the king an "Olive Branch Petition" in July 1775, King George refused to read it. He said the petition had come from ___traitors___ and rebels.

4. On August 23, 1775, King George issued his fatal proclamation declaring that a "general rebellion" existed in the colonies—a rebellion that was to be subdued by the "utmost endeavors." He said that the rebel leaders were to be arrested as traitors and brought to justice (which meant execution). Men like Sam Adams and John Hancock had a price on their heads.

5. On December 22, 1775, the king issued an even harsher proclamation which virtually abolished the colonists' status as British ___subjects___. The king said that the Americans were to be treated as enemies, and that all trade with the colonies was outlawed. American ships could be seized, their cargoes confiscated, and their crews drafted into the British navy.

B. This brings us to the crisis year of 1776.

John Dickinson

We usually think of 1776 as one of the most glorious years in American history. But at the time it did not seem very glorious to the Founding Fathers. Some considered it one of the worst years in America's formative period.

I

A. News came that the Americans had lost the campaign in ___Canada___.

1. After capturing Montreal, the Americans had lost the battle of Quebec.

By his EXCELLENCY
WILLIAM TRYON, Esquire,

Captain General, and Governor in Chief in and over the Province of *New-York*, and the Territories depending thereon in *America*, Chancellor and Vice Admiral of the fame.

A PROCLAMATION.

WHEREAS I have received His Majefty's Royal Proclamation, given at the Court at *St. James's*, the Twenty-third Day of *Auguft* laft, in the Words following:

BY THE KING,
A Proclamation,

For fuppreffing REBELLION and SEDITION.

GEORGE R.

WHEREAS many of our Subjects in divers Parts of our Colonies and Plantations in *North-America*, misled by dangerous and ill defigning Men, and forgetting the Allegiance which they owe to the Power that has protected and fuftained them, after various diforderly Acts committed in difturbance of the public Peace, to the Obftruction of lawful Commerce, and to the Oppreffion of our loyal Subjects carrying on the fame, have at length proceeded to an open and avowed Rebellion, by arraying themfelves in hoftile Manner, to withftand the Execution of the Law, and traitoroufly preparing, ordering and levying War againft us: And whereas there is Reafon to apprehend that fuch Rebellion hath been much promoted and encouraged by the traitorous Correfpondence, Counfels, and Comfort of divers wicked and defperate Perfons within this Realm :—To the End therefore that none of our Subjects may neglect or violate their Duty through Ignorance thereof, or through any Doubt of the Protection which the Law will afford to their Loyalty and Zeal ; we have thought fit, by and with the Advice of our Privy Council, to iffue this our Royal Proclamation, hereby declaring, that not only all our Officers Civil and Military, are obliged to exert their utmoft Endeavours to fupprefs fuch Rebellion, and to bring the Traitors to Juftice ; but that all our Subjects of this Realm and the Dominions thereunto belonging, are bound by Law to be aiding and affifting in the Suppreffion of fuch Rebellion, and to difclofe and make known all traitorous Confpiracies and Attempts againft us, our Crown and Dignity : And we do accordingly ftrictly charge and command all our Officers, as well Civil as Military, and all other our obedient and loyal Subjects, to ufe their utmoft Endeavours to withftand and fupprefs fuch Rebellion, and to difclofe and make known all Treafons and traitorous Confpiracies which they fhall know to be againft us, our Crown and Dignity ; and for that Purpofe, that they tranfmit to one of our principal Secretaries of State, or other proper Officer, due and full Information of all Perfons who fhall be found carrying on Correfpondence with, or in any Manner or Degree aiding or abetting the Perfons now in open Arms and Rebellion againft our Government within any of our Colonies and Plantations in *North-America*, in order to bring to condign Punifhment the Authors, Perpetrators, and Abettors of fuch traitorous Defigns.

Given at our Court at St. James's the Twenty-third Day of Auguft, One Thoufand Seven Hundred and Seventy-five, in the Fifteenth Year of our Reign.

In Obedience therefore to his Majefty's Commands 'to me given, I do hereby publifh and make known his Majefty's moft gracious Proclamation above recited ; earneftly exhorting and requiring all his Majefty's loyal and faithful Subjects within this Province, as they value their Allegiance due to the beft of Sovereigns, their Dependance on and Protection from their Parent State, and the Bleffings of a mild, free, and happy Conftitution ; and as they would fhun the fatal Calamities which are the inevitable Confequences of Sedition and Rebellion, to pay all due Obedience to the Laws of their Country, ferioufly to attend to his Majefty's faid Proclamation, and govern themfelves accordingly.

Given under my Hand and Seal at Arms, in the City of New-York, the Fourteenth Day of November, One Thoufand Seven Hundred and Seventy-five, in the Sixteenth Year of the Reign of our Sovereign Lord George the Third, by the Grace of God of Great-Britain, France and Ireland, King, Defender of the Faith, and fo forth.

WM. TRYON.

By his Excellency's Command,
SAMUEL BAYARD, Jun. D. Secry.

GOD SAVE THE KING.

2. General Montgomery had been killed, and Benedict Arnold, who had been a hero in the battle, was badly wounded.

3. Within a few months, all American forces had retreated from Canada to rejoin Washington's continental forces.

B. Meanwhile, during the siege of Boston, more than _4,000_ of Washington's badly needed troops left him.

1. Of those who were left, many were sick.

2. Enlistments were only for six months, and as soon as their time was up,

few of the soldiers reenlisted.

    3. Morale was low. Since the British would not come out and fight after the severe losses at Bunker Hill, the Americans had little activity except to fight among themselves!

C. The American colonies found that they had been virtually _disowned_ by King George III.

    1. He had announced that if the rebellious American colonies were attacked, Britain would not come to their aid.

    2. As previously mentioned, not only were American ships declared by the king to be free booty to anyone who could capture them, but American crews were "impressed" or forced into the British navy to help capture more American ships.

D. By 1776, many leaders in the colonies recognized that circumstances might force them into a state of separate independence from Britain without a single colony knowing how to _govern_ itself.

    1. Virginia, the largest state in population, was expected to lead the way in discovering the best form of independent government.

    2. However, Virginia had already examined _6_ different drafts for a practical constitution and was still uncertain as to which one was best.

    3. Jefferson rejected all of them. He was one of the foremost constitutionalists in the world, but he was greatly distressed to learn that very few scholars of that day were prepared to support what he felt needed to be done.

Why was 1776 such a terribly _difficult_ year for Thomas Jefferson?

A. A daughter had recently died.

B. His wife was extremely ill.

C. His mother died on March 31.

D. His sorrow and worry over the state of the country gave him severe migraine headaches which lasted five weeks.

E. He was especially worried about Virginia working out a sound system of self-government.

    1. He wrote _3_ constitutional drafts in _5_ weeks.

    2. All but a small section of the third draft was rejected by the Virginia Legislature.

    3. Virginia adopted a temporary constitution retaining most of the _weaknesses_ existing under British rule:

        a. Slavery.

        b. Primogeniture—a rule under which inherited property went exclusively to the oldest _son_.

        c. Entailed estates—making it unlawful for heirs to divide huge feudal estates.

II

Thomas Jefferson

> d. The official state church was left in power.
>
> e. People were _____toxed_____ to support the official church whether or not they were members.

III

By 1776, Jefferson had already discovered the basic success formula that was eventually incorporated into the Constitution of the United States. Although he might not have realized it at the time, he was going to have supreme difficulty getting these ideas accepted. Nevertheless, he was probably the best prepared of all the Founders to launch the campaign. His educational background was remarkable, even by modern standards.

A. He had begun studying Latin, Greek, and French at the age of 9. At the age of 16 he entered the College of William and Mary at Williamsburg. At 18 he graduated and began to be tutored in law by George Wythe, the first professor of law in America. During a five-year period he often studied 12 to 14 hours a day. When he was examined for the bar, he knew more than the men who were giving him the exam.

B. Here is a summary of his educational background:

1. He had gained proficiency in ___5___ languages.

2. He had studied the ___Roman___ classics.

3. He had studied the ___Greek___ classics.

4. He had studied European ___history___.

5. He had carefully studied the Old and New Testaments.

6. While studying the history of ancient Israel, Jefferson made an astonishing discovery. He saw that at one time the Israelites had

Jefferson's home at Monticello, Virginia.

practiced the earliest and most efficient form of __representative__ government. So long as they followed a fixed pattern of constitutional principles, they flourished; when they drifted from it, disaster overtook them. Jefferson thereafter referred to this constitutional pattern as the "__Ancient__ __Principles__."

7. Jefferson was also surprised to find that the Anglo-Saxons were aware of the same "ancient principles" and followed a pattern almost __identical__ with that of the Israelites until the eighth century A.D. In our next lesson we will discuss the pattern which both of these nations followed.

8. Jefferson undertook a thorough study of __British__ history, which demonstrated that in a period of a thousand years the English people had done more than any other nation to revive human freedom on earth.

C. Jefferson's years of intensive study made the following impression on a stranger who did not know who he was:

When he spoke of law, I thought he was a lawyer; when he talked about mechanics, I was sure he was an engineer; when he got into medicine, it was evident that he was a physician; when he discussed theology, I was convinced he must be a clergyman; when he talked of literature, I made up my mind that I had run against a college professor who knew everything. (William E. Curtis, *The True Thomas Jefferson*, Philadelphia: J. B. Lippincott Company, 1901, pp. 358–59.)

Jefferson was caught up in the spirit of independence that rose sharply throughout the colonies during the spring of 1776.

IV

A. In 1776, Thomas Paine, who had arrived in America only two years earlier, published a pamphlet called __Common__ __Sense__, in which he advocated immediate independence. More than 120,000 copies of his pamphlet were sold in a short time—a phenomenal circulation for those days. George Washington said that this little pamphlet "worked a powerful change in the minds of many men."

B. On March ___17___, 1776, Washington's forces liberated Boston.

C. On May ___4___, 1776, Rhode Island jumped the gun and declared independence all by herself.

D. On May ___10___, 1776, Congress authorized each colony to set up its own government independent of the crown, because the king said he had disowned them.

E. On May ___14___, 1776, Jefferson arrived in Philadelphia as a delegate to Congress, but his heart was in Virginia where the House of Burgesses was trying to decide what kind of constitution a free people should have.

F. Jefferson almost missed writing the Declaration of Independence by requesting permission to return to Virginia to work on the new constitution for that state. His request was ___denied___.

G. On June ___7___, 1776, Richard Henry Lee introduced a resolution calling upon the colonies to declare themselves free and independent states. The final vote was postponed until some of the delegates could return home for instructions. They agreed to return by July 2.

H. On June ___11___, 1776, a special committee was appointed to write a formal declaration of independence. The members included Thomas Jefferson (Virginia), John Adams (Massachusetts), Benjamin Franklin (Pennsylvania), Roger Sherman (Connecticut), and Robert Livingston (New York).

The house in Philadelphia where Jefferson wrote the Declaration.

Members of the committee: Franklin, Jefferson, Livingston, Adams, and Sherman.

Writing the Declaration of Independence.

V

A. A conversation between John Adams and Thomas Jefferson was recorded by Adams as follows:

> "Jefferson proposed to me to make the draft. I said: I will not. You should do it."
>
> Jefferson: "Oh, no! Why will you not? You ought to do it."
>
> Adams: "I will not!"
>
> Jefferson: "Why?"
>
> Adams: "Reasons enough."
>
> Jefferson: "What can be your reasons?"
>
> Adams: "Reason first—You are a Virginian, and a Virginian ought to appear at the head of this business. Reason second—I am obnoxious, suspected, and unpopular. You are very much otherwise. Reason third—You can write ten times better than I can."
>
> Jefferson: "Well, if you are decided, I will do as well as I can." (Charles Francis Adams, ed., *The Works of John Adams*, 10 vols., Boston: Little, Brown and Co., 1850–56, 2:51n.)

B. For ___17___ days Jefferson worked on the draft, with nearly all of the time being spent on the first two paragraphs.

    1. The charges against King George, which took up most of the draft, were copied almost entirely from the drafts of his constitution of Virginia and his *Summary View of the Rights of British America*. This would not have required more than ___1___ day. What was he doing the other 16 days?

    2. Jefferson's great anxiety seems to have been to get into the Declaration of Independence the most basic elements of the "ancient principles" mentioned in his proposed drafts for the Virginia state constitution.

C. Here are the eight "ancient principles" which Jefferson incorporated in the first ___2___ paragraphs of the Declaration of Independence. These are rounded out in some of his subsequent writings to provide a fuller understanding of each principle:

    1. Sound government should be based on ___Self___-___evident___ truths—truths that are so obvious, so rational, and so morally sound that their authenticity is beyond reasonable dispute.

    2. The government of mankind here on earth should be based on the law of ___nature___ and of nature's God.

    3. This presupposes (as a self-evident truth) that the Creator made human beings ___equal___ in their rights, equal before the bar of justice, and equal in his sight. (Of course, individual attributes and personal circumstances in life vary widely.)

    4. These rights, which have been bestowed by the Creator on each

Part of Jefferson's original draft of the Declaration of Independence.

individual, are _ina Cienable_ ; that is, they cannot be taken away or violated without the offender coming under the judgment and wrath of God. A person may have other rights, such as those which have been created as a "vested" right by a statute, but vested rights are not inalienable. They can be altered or eliminated at any time.

5. Among the most important of the inalienable rights are the right to life, the right to liberty, and the right to pursue whatever course of life a person may desire in search of happiness, property, and peace, so long as it does not invade the rights of _others_ .

6. The most basic reason for a community or a nation to set up a system of government is to assure its inhabitants that these special rights of the people shall be _protected_ and preserved.

7. And because this is so, it follows that no office or agency of government

has any right to exist except with the ___consent___ of the people or their representatives.

8. It also follows that if a government, either by malfeasance or neglect, fails to protect those rights—or, even worse, if the government itself begins to violate those rights—then it is the right and ___duty___ of the people to regain control of their affairs and set up a form of government which will serve the people better.

D. On July 4, 1776, Congress adopted the Declaration of Independence after making ___60___ changes but not deleting a single one of Jefferson's "ancient principles."

1. A copy was immediately sent to a Mr. Dunlap for printing, and an official copy was engrossed (written in large formal script) for signing. The delegates began signing the engrossed copy on August 2. This is the copy now on display in the Archives Building in Washington, D.C. The original copy that was sent to the printer has been ___lost___.

2. The Declaration was published by the Pennsylvania *Evening Post* on July 6, and the first public reading was by the Committee on Correspondence in Philadelphia on July 8. People cheered, bells rang, and many celebrated all night.

3. Jefferson was not originally identified as the ___author___. The identity of the signers was also kept concealed for several months for fear of retaliation by the British.

4. All those who subscribed to the Declaration figuratively signed the

The first public reading of the Declaration, July 8, 1776, from the steps of Independence Hall in Philadelphia.

document with their _____Blood_____. In support of the Declaration, they had mutually pledged "our lives, our fortunes, and our sacred honor."

    a. Had they lost the Revolutionary War, they would, no doubt, have been tried and summarily convicted of high _____treason_____.

    b. The penalty for high treason was to be hanged from the gallows until unconscious, then cut down and _____revived_____, then disemboweled and beheaded, then cut into quarters, each quarter to be boiled in oil and the residue spread over the countryside so that the last resting place of the offender would be forever unnamed, unhonored, and unknown.

VI — Jefferson reveals the source of his "ancient principles."

A. After writing the Declaration of Independence, Jefferson was appointed to a special committee with Benjamin Franklin and John Adams to prepare an official seal for the United States.

B. Both Jefferson and Franklin suggested that one side of the seal portray Moses leading ancient Israel, since the Israelites had the historical distinction of being the most ancient people to practice the principles of _____representative_____ government.

C. John Adams felt that since Jefferson had discovered that the Anglo-Saxons had practiced almost _____identical_____ principles, they also should be represented on the other side of the seal. Adams wrote:

> Mr. Jefferson proposed: The children of Israel in the wilderness, led by a cloud by day, and a pillar of fire by night, and on the other side Hengist and Horsa, the Saxon chiefs, from whom we claim the honour of being descended and whose political principles and form of government we have assumed. (Richard S. Patterson and Richardson Dougall, *The Eagle and the Shield: A History of the Great Seal of the United States,* Washington: U.S. Department of State, 1976, p. 16.)

Original proposal for the seal of the United States as suggested by Thomas Jefferson, Benjamin Franklin, and John Adams.

D. Professor Gilbert Chinard, one of the distinguished biographers of Jefferson, states:

> Jefferson's great ambition at that time was to promote a renaissance of _Anglo_ - _Saxon_ primitive institutions on the new continent. Thus presented, the American Revolution was nothing but the reclamation of the Anglo-Saxon birthright of which the colonists had been deprived by 'a long train of abuses.' Nor does it appear that there was anything in this theory which surprised or shocked his contemporaries; Adams apparently did not disapprove of it, and it would be easy to bring in many similar expressions of the same idea in documents of the time. (Gilbert Chinard, *Thomas Jefferson: The Apostle of Americanism,* Ann Arbor, Mich: University of Michigan Press, 1964, pp. 86–87.)

E. In his *Summary View of the Rights of British America,* Jefferson wrote that their "Saxon ancestors had...possessed themselves of the Island of Britain...and had established there that system of laws which has so long been the glory and protection of that country." (Saul K. Padover, *The Complete Jefferson,* New York: Tudor Publishing Co., 1943, pp. 6–7.)

F. On August 13, 1776, Jefferson wrote to Edmund Pendleton to convince him that Virginia must _abolish_ the remnants of feudalism and return to the "ancient principles." He wrote:

> Are we not better for what we have hitherto abolished of the feudal system? Has not every restitution of the ancient Saxon laws had happy effects? Is it not better now that we return at once into that happy system of our ancestors, the wisest and most perfect ever yet devised by the wit of man, as it stood before the eighth century? (Julian P. Boyd, ed., *The Papers of Thomas Jefferson,* 20 vols. by 1982, Princeton, N.J.: Princeton University Press, 1950–, 1:492.)

G. Jefferson studied the language of the Anglo-Saxons so that he might read their laws in the original tongue. In a letter to his old tutor, George Wythe,

Two sides of the official seal of the United States.

dated November 1, 1778, Jefferson wrote that "the extracts from the Anglo-Saxon law, the sources of the Common law, I wrote in the original for my own satisfaction; but I have added Latin or liberal English translations." (Ibid., 2:504.)

H. Congress finally adopted a more simple seal with the American _eagle_ on one side and an unfinished _pyramid_ of thirteen steps on the other (representing the thirteen original colonies and copied from the fifty-dollar bill of the Continental currency used during the Revolutionary War). At the bottom of the pyramid were inscribed the Roman numerals for 1776, and the all-seeing eye of the Creator appeared at the top. There were also two classical Latin mottoes: *Annuit Coeptis* ' _He_ Hath Favored Our Undertaking,' and *Novus Ordo Seclorum* ' _New_ Order of the Ages' or 'Beginning of a New Age.'

3

How Thomas Jefferson Discovered America's Great Success Formula

Introduction

We have already seen why the early part of 1776 was considered by the Founding Fathers to have been one of the most difficult intervals of the Revolutionary War period. However, nothing in the early part of that year could compare with the stream of disasters that struck the American forces during the latter part of 1776.

At the height of this crisis Thomas Jefferson felt compelled to make a monumental decision.

I

A. During the summer of 1776 the British mobilized, under General William Howe, the largest _army_ that had ever been assembled on the North American continent. The British also brought over the largest _fleet_ that had ever been seen in the Western Hemisphere, commanded by General Howe's brother, Admiral Lord Richard Howe.

B. The battle for New York went badly. Without a _navy_, Washington could do little more than put up a token resistance. By August 29 the Americans had been driven from Long Island, and by September 12 they had been forced to abandon the city of New York with its population of 22,000 (making it the second largest city in the country, next to _Philadelphia_). On September 21 the city was virtually burned to the ground, though the source of the fire was not known. Washington retreated toward White Plains.

Washington directs the retreat from Long Island.

C. It was in the midst of this crisis that Jefferson _resigned_ from Congress and returned to Virginia. He had two compelling reasons:

1. The continued _illness_ of his wife had been accentuated by two recent deaths in the family.

2. Although Jefferson was confident that the Americans would win the war, he was fearful that the states would not know what to do with their freedom once they had it. He did not feel that any of the states were prepared either psychologically or constitutionally to take on the burden of self-government so that they could preserve their freedom.

D. He was frustrated that the constitution adopted by Virginia was not a charter of freedom but a legislative attempt to institutionalize the _evils_ which had existed under the crown.

E. The very fact that the Virginia legislature had rejected his constitutional drafts reflected their reluctance to eliminate slavery and establish a true charter of _equality_ and _freedom_ for all.

F. Jefferson seemed to sense that before a genuine republican form of government could be instituted, a campaign must be launched to clear out the accumulated rubbish of feudalism, aristocracy, slavery, and the worst parts of the British statutory law which had been _inherited_ by Virginia from England.

G. After putting his family affairs in order, Jefferson rejected an opportunity to go to France as an American diplomatic officer and, instead, sought election to the state legislature in Williamsburg. There he succeeded in having a number of committees set up to reform the whole structure of law and government in Virginia. Although it took many years to get his reforms adopted, here is what Jefferson initiated in a brief period of only _2_ years:

1. He set up a formula for abolishing _slavery_ by peaceful means within one generation.

2. He revised the _civil_ code.

3. He revised the _criminal_ code.

4. He introduced a bill to abolish primogeniture, a feudal law requiring a parent to bestow his entire estate on his _eldest_ son whether or not he was competent.

5. He introduced a bill to _abolish_ entail estates—a feudal practice

which required that large tracts of land be maintained intact in a family because of obligations to the king or some high-ranking lord or baron.

6. He introduced a bill to eliminate the _____death_____ penalty, except for murder, treason, and certain military crimes in time of war.

7. He introduced a bill to eliminate _____cruel_____ and unusual punishment.

Cruel and unusual punishment was forbidden in America.

8. He introduced a bill to eliminate the official recognition of a state church so that there could be equality for all religions.

9. He introduced a bill to eliminate the payment of a tithing tax to support a particular church.

H. In June 1783, just as the Revolutionary War came to a close, Jefferson composed his _fourth_ and final draft for a sound system of government in Virginia. He took it with him when he accepted an appointment as minister to France and finally published it there.

II It had been a difficult and painstaking process to sift out the golden nuggets of "ancient principles" for the American _success_ formula.

A. The pilgrimage of exploration into the past was pursued by many of the Founders including Jefferson, Madison, Franklin, Samuel Adams, John Adams, and James Wilson. Not only were many of the Founders excellent scholars and widely read, but they exchanged correspondence and cross-fertilized their thinking for a quarter of a century before they put it all together in the _Constitution_.

B. Some of the voluminous major works through which Jefferson and several of the other Founders had patiently plowed included the writings of Plato, Aristotle, Polybius, Cicero, Richard Hooker, Edward Coke, Thomas Hobbes, Algernon Sidney, John Locke, Baron Charles de Montesquieu, David Hume, and William Blackstone.

C. The Founders developed a yardstick for measuring the merits of government:

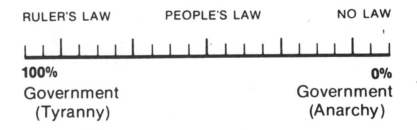

RULER'S LAW	PEOPLE'S LAW	NO LAW

100%
Government
(Tyranny)

0%
Government
(Anarchy)

1. George Washington described the human struggle wherein "there is a natural and necessary progression from the extreme of _anarchy_ to the extreme of _tyranny_." (John C. Fitzpatrick, ed., *The Writings of George Washington*, 39 vols., Washington: United States Government Printing Office, 1931–44, 26:489.)

2. Thomas Jefferson emphasized the same point: "We are now vibrating between too much and too little government, and the pendulum will rest finally in the _middle_." (Paul Leicester Ford, ed., *The Writings of Thomas Jefferson*, 10 vols., New York: G. P. Putnam's Sons, 1892–99, 5:3.)

D. The Founders knew from sad experience that the foremost enemy of freedom and self-government is Ruler's Law, with its power base of central government hanging menacingly over the people:

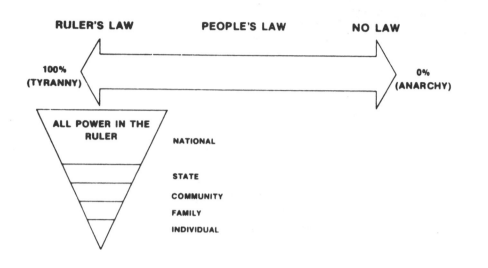

RULER'S LAW   PEOPLE'S LAW   NO LAW

100%
(TYRANNY)   0%
                                        (ANARCHY)

ALL POWER IN THE RULER

NATIONAL

STATE

COMMUNITY

FAMILY

INDIVIDUAL

The Founders had studied Ruler's Law and knew its chief characteristics:

1. Government control is exercised by force, conquest, or legislative usurpation.

2. Therefore, all power is concentrated in the ___ruler___.

3. The people are treated as "subjects" of the ruler.

4. The land is treated as the "realm'" of the ruler.

5. The people have no inalienable rights.

6. Government is by the rule of ___men___ rather than the rule of law.

7. The people are structured into social and economic classes.

8. The thrust of government is always from the ruler down, not from the people upward.

9. Problems are typically solved by issuing new edicts, creating more bureaus, appointing more administrators, and charging the people more ___taxes___ to pay for these "services." Under this system, taxes and government regulations are oppressive.

10. Freedom is not considered a solution to anything.

11. The transfer of power from one ruler to another is often by ___violence___—the dagger, the poison cup, or fratricidal civil war.

12. The long history of Ruler's Law is one of blood and terror, both anciently and in modern times. Those in power revel in luxury while the lot of the common people is one of perpetual poverty, excessive taxation, stringent regulations, and a continuous existence of ___misery___.

E. Jefferson and the other Founders hoped to find the golden mean in the center of the political spectrum. The idea was to have the governing power based in the *people* themselves, with a hierarchy of limited government serving them. The political structure they visualized would look something like this:

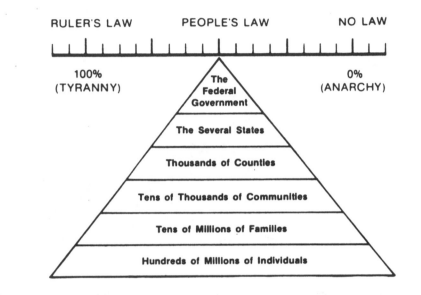

RULER'S LAW   PEOPLE'S LAW   NO LAW

100%
(TYRANNY)

0%
(ANARCHY)

The Federal Government

The Several States

Thousands of Counties

Tens of Thousands of Communities

Tens of Millions of Families

Hundreds of Millions of Individuals

F. Once the government was established, the Founders hoped to keep it in the balanced *center* under the control of the people. This would require a written constitution. However, since no pattern for such a government existed anywhere in the world, they had to either discover some example of it from past history or invent one through their own ingenuity. In the final analysis, what they were seeking was a system of *Peoples* Law to replace the tyranny of Ruler's Law.

G. Thomas *Jefferson* was one of the first to make the long pilgrimage into the past trying to find the right answers.

H. Why was Jefferson so fascinated with the development of People's Law depicted in the history of ancient Israel?

 1. The Israelites came out of Egypt sometime between 1490 and 1290 B.C.

 2. They were originally under Ruler's Law, which was the only system the

people had known while in Egypt. The role of Moses as the leader under Ruler's Law might be graphically illustrated as follows:

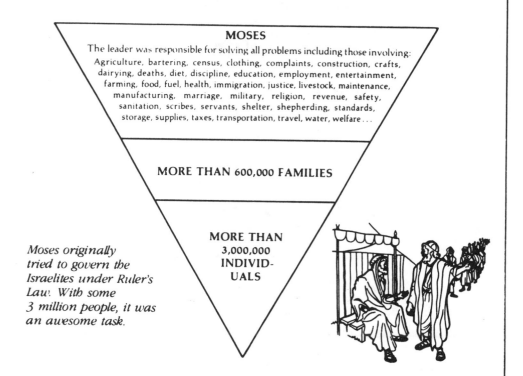

MOSES
The leader was responsible for solving all problems including those involving:
Agriculture, bartering, census, clothing, complaints, construction, crafts, dairying, deaths, diet, discipline, education, employment, entertainment, farming, food, fuel, health, immigration, justice, livestock, maintenance, manufacturing, marriage, military, religion, revenue, safety, sanitation, scribes, servants, shelter, shepherding, standards, storage, supplies, taxes, transportation, travel, water, welfare . . .

MORE THAN 600,000 FAMILIES

MORE THAN 3,000,000 INDIVIDUALS

Moses originally tried to govern the Israelites under Ruler's Law. With some 3 million people, it was an awesome task.

3. Moses found it impossible to govern the people effectively under this system. The record says that the people lined up "from morning unto the evening" (Exodus 18:13) to have Moses solve their problems.

4. Jethro, Moses' father-in-law, said, "The thing that thou doest is not good. Thou wilt surely wear away, both thou, and this people that is with thee: for this thing is too heavy for thee; thou art not able to perform it thyself alone." (Exodus 18:17–18.)

5. Jethro then instructed Moses on the way he should organize this multitude of approximately 3 million people.

6. Following the advice of Jethro, Moses divided the people (consisting of about 600,000 families) into groups of 10 families each. Then he had each group elect a leader or "judge" to preside over them. These small groups were combined in groups of 50 families, each of which also elected a leader. Then, these larger groups were combined into companies of 100 families, and they too elected a leader. Finally, these combinations were formed into groups of 1,000 families, each of which again elected a leader. All of these leaders were to be "able men, such as fear God, men of truth, hating covetousness." (Exodus 18:21.)

7. By this means, the people were organized into small, manageable groups with elected "rulers of thousands, rulers of hundreds, rulers of fifties, and rulers of ten." (Exodus 18:25.)

"Servile Pyramid"

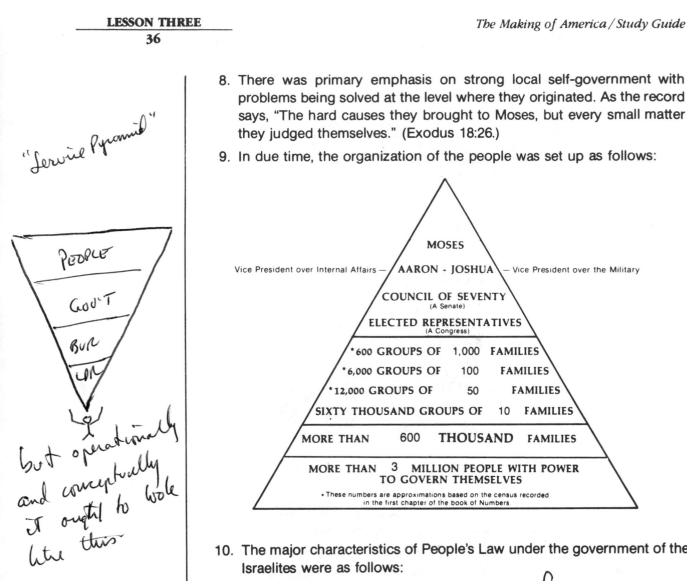

PEOPLE

GOV'T

BUR

LAW

but operationally
and conceptually
it ought to look
like this

8. There was primary emphasis on strong local self-government with problems being solved at the level where they originated. As the record says, "The hard causes they brought to Moses, but every small matter they judged themselves." (Exodus 18:26.)

9. In due time, the organization of the people was set up as follows:

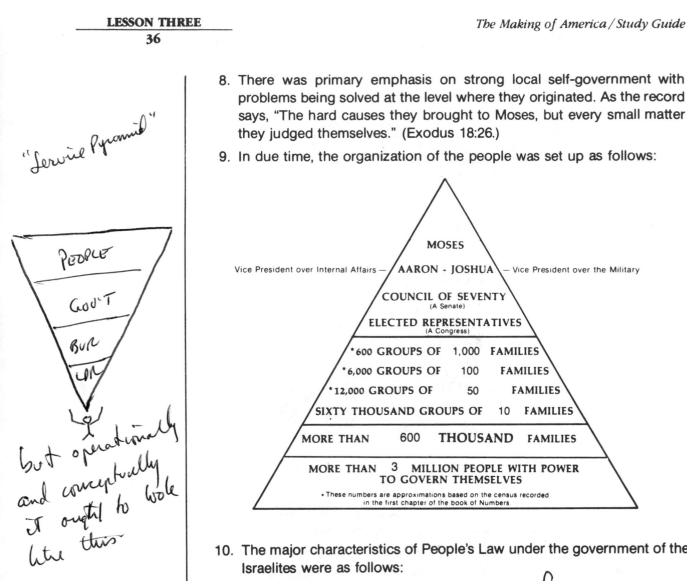

MOSES

Vice President over Internal Affairs — AARON - JOSHUA — Vice President over the Military

COUNCIL OF SEVENTY
(A Senate)

ELECTED REPRESENTATIVES
(A Congress)

*600 GROUPS OF 1,000 FAMILIES

*6,000 GROUPS OF 100 FAMILIES

*12,000 GROUPS OF 50 FAMILIES

SIXTY THOUSAND GROUPS OF 10 FAMILIES

MORE THAN 600 **THOUSAND** FAMILIES

MORE THAN 3 MILLION PEOPLE WITH POWER TO GOVERN THEMSELVES

* These numbers are approximations based on the census recorded in the first chapter of the book of Numbers

10. The major characteristics of People's Law under the government of the Israelites were as follows:

a. They were set up as a commonwealth of _freemen_, a system reflected in the command: "Proclaim liberty throughout all the land unto all the inhabitants thereof." (Leviticus 25:10.)

Whenever the Israelites fell into the temptation to have slaves or bond servants, they were reprimanded. Around 600 B.C., a divine reprimand was given through Jeremiah: "Ye have not hearkened unto me, in proclaiming liberty, every one to his brother, and every man to his neighbor: behold, I proclaim a liberty for you, saith the Lord." (Jeremiah 34:17.)

b. The duties and responsibilities of the people were based on religious principles and a solid commitment to ~~morality~~ _morality_. (See Exodus 20:2–17.)

(1) Benjamin Franklin declared: "Only a virtuous people are capable of freedom. As nations become corrupt and vicious, they have more need of masters." (Albert Henry Smith, *The Writings of Benjamin Franklin,* 10 vols., New York: Macmillan Co., 1905–7, 9:569.)

(2) John Adams was equally explicit: "Our Constitution was made only for a moral and religious people. It is wholly inadequate to the government of any other." (John R. Howe, *The Changing Political Thought of John Adams,* Princeton, N.J.: Princeton University Press, 1966, p. 189.)

80 yrs old

c. They were organized in small, manageable units where everyone had a voice and a ___vote___.

d. There was a major emphasis on strong local self-government.

e. They had a system of honest ___money___.

f. The land was looked upon as a private stewardship of the people, not the government.

g. The rights of property were protected.

h. The rights of life and private liberty were protected.

i. All ___leaders___ were selected with the consent of a majority of the people. (See 2 Samuel 2:4; 1 Chronicles 29:22; for the rejection of a leader, see 2 Chronicles 10:16.)

j. All ___laws___ came into force only when approved by a majority of the people or their representatives. (Exodus 19:8.)

k. Accused persons were presumed to be innocent until proven guilty. Evidence had to be strong enough to remove any question of doubt. Borderline cases were decided in favor of the accused and left to the judgment of ___God___.

l. The entire code of justice was based primarily on reparation to the _____victim_____ rather than fines and punishment by the commonwealth. (Reference to this procedure will be found in Exodus 21 and 22.) The one crime for which no "satisfaction" could be given was first-degree murder. The penalty was death. (Numbers 35:31.)

m. The main thrust of government was from the people upward; only in a time of temporary crisis was the thrust from the government down. (The Founders included this in the Constitution in their enumeration of the _____War_____ powers.)

n. The government was required to operate according to principles of _____law_____, not the whims of men.

o. Because this system expressed the will of the majority of the people, it allowed power to be transferred from one regime to another by _____Peaceful_____ means.

III The Israelites occupied much of Palestine until around 922 B.C., when ten of the tribes broke away from the two remaining tribes of Judah and Levi. During 722–21 B.C., the northern ten tribes were captured by Assyria and carried off to

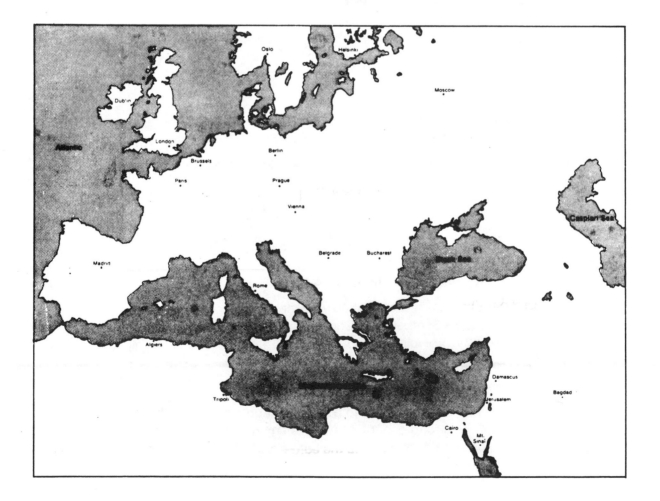

that country. When the Assyrians were conquered by the Babylonians in 605 B.C., the ten tribes were able to escape northward where they settled around the ___Black Sea___. In due time they disappeared from history as a people and are usually referred to as the lost Ten Tribes.

Why was Thomas Jefferson equally fascinated with the development of People's Law by the Anglo-Saxons?   **IV**

A. The Anglo-Saxons trace their beginnings back to a people who called themselves "Yinglings," later changed to "Engels" and then "Anglos." According to the *Saga of the Norse Kings,* the Yinglings came from the area of the Black Sea, exactly where the Ten Tribes were located before they disappeared.

B. They left the Black Sea area about 65 B.C. as ___Romans___ legions began conquering the territory. They spread all across Northern Europe. After conquering and intermingling with the Saxons, they were called Anglo-Saxons.

C. The Anglo-Saxons began migrating to Britain around A.D. 450. They conquered the ___Celts___ (including King Arthur) and changed the name of the island from Britain to England. The first Anglo-Saxons to bring their system of People's Law to England were two brothers named Hengist and Horsa.

D. The Anglo-Saxons were the best organized people in Europe and soon spread their influence into nearly every European country. Anglo-Saxons in the north became known as ___Vikings___. They not only occupied all of Scandanavia but soon took over Iceland, discovered Greenland, and then went on to establish colonies in North America 500 years before Columbus. However, they died out for some unknown reason long before Columbus arrived.

E. Many have thought the Yinglings, or Anglos, included a branch of the ancient Israelites because they came from the territory of the Black Sea and because they preserved by some means the same unique institutes of ___Government___ as those which were given to the Israelites at Mount Sinai. (See Colin Rhys Lovell, *English Constitutional and Legal History,* New York: Oxford University Press, 1962.)

1. They considered themselves a commonwealth of ___freemen___.

2. They organized themselves into units identical to those of the Israelites:

   a. The head of 10 families was called a ___tithing man___.

   b. The head of 50 families became an obscure office but may have been a vil-man, or head of a ___village___.

   c. The head of 100 families was called the ___hundred___ man.

   d. The head of 1,000 families was called the eolderman, later shortened to ___earl___. The territory occupied by 1,000 families was called a shire, and the administrative assistant to the earl was called the "shire reef." We pronounce it ___Sheriff___.

3. All laws, as well as the election of leaders, had to be by the common ___consent___ of the people.

4. Authority granted to a chieftain in time of war was extremely ___limited___ and was taken away from him as soon as the emergency had passed.

5. Their system of justice was based on payment of damages to the ___victim___ rather than calling it a crime against the whole people.

V Having discovered what John Adams later called the "divine science" or ___natural___ law of sound government, the Founders wondered if there were natural laws which would produce a dynamic and prosperous economy with a high standard of living.

A. In 1776, just as the first free people in modern times was coming into existence as the United States of America, an economist in Scotland (a friend of Benjamin Franklin) published his now famous book, *The Wealth of Nations.* His name was Adam Smith.

B. In his book, Adam Smith said wealth is not ___Gold___ and ___Silver___ but the essentials of life—food, clothes, houses, transportation, communications, schools, good roads, factories, and well-cultivated farms.

C. Adam Smith said that if you want an increased standard of living and prosperity, goods and services should be ___abundant___ and ___cheap___. How is that achieved? Here are the highlights of Adam Smith's formula:

1. Specialized ___Production___.

2. Buying and selling in a ___free___ market.

3. Based on the natural law of ___supply___ and ___demand___, where people vote with their dollars on what they want or don't want. Natural-law marketing is completely democratic.

4. Everyone improves his position by making a ___profit___ at whatever he is doing. A profit is defined as doing whatever is necessary to make an exchange ___worthwhile___.

5. The secret to the successful operation of a free market is COMPETITION. It is painful, but the results are good:

   a. Greater ___quantity___ (more production, more profit).

   b. Improved ~~prices~~ quality (to attract customers).

   c. Lower ~~quantity~~ prices (to beat the competition).

   d. A greater ___~~~~___ of goods and services to satisfy individual customer demands. ___variety___

Adam Smith

6. The greatest threat to a free-market economy is government ___*intolerance*___. This happens when the government is involved in fixing *prices*, fixing *wages*, controlling *production*, controlling *distribution*, or subsidizing production. The role of government is simply to serve as referee and to prevent:

a. ___*illegal*___ ___*force*___ (Mafia tactics).

b. ___*fraud*___ (phony stocks and bonds).

c. ___*Monopoly*___ (eliminating competition).

d. ___*debauchery*___ (pornography, obscenity, drugs, prostitution, and other forms of ___*vice*___).

D. Adam Smith's tremendously successful formula for prosperity can be summarized in the following economic principles:

1. The freedom to ___*try*___.
2. The freedom to ___*buy*___.
3. The freedom to ___*sell*___.
4. The freedom to ___*fail*___.

E. When Adam Smith published his new book, no country in the world was practicing free-market economics. The United States was the ___*FIRST*___ nation to try it.

F. Thomas Jefferson later rejoiced in the tremendous success of the ___*natural*___ laws that had led to the development of a prosperous free-enterprise economy in America. These were the laws Adam Smith had endeavored to enunciate in *The Wealth of Nations.* Jefferson declared:

> We remark with special satisfaction those [prosperous circumstances] which, under the smiles of Providence, result from the skill, industry, and order of our citizens, managing their own affairs in their own way and for their own use, unembarrassed by too [many] regulations, unoppressed by fiscal exactions. (Second Annual Message to Congress, in Albert Ellery Bergh, ed., *The Writings of Thomas Jefferson,* 20 vols., Washington: Thomas Jefferson Memorial Association, 1907, 3:340.)

Agriculture, manufactures, commerce, and navigation, the four pillars

of our prosperity, are the most thriving when left most free to individual enterprise. (First Annual Message to Congress, in ibid., p. 337.)

Conclusion

It was a monumental task to glean from history the natural laws of freedom, security, and prosperity. It was an even greater task to put the principles into practical operation. We now turn to the slow and sporadic effort to provide a proper structure for the American success formula.

4

How the First U.S. Constitution Almost Lost the Revolutionary War

Introduction

Once the Founding Fathers made the decision to declare independence, they knew they had to formulate a structure of government that would unite the states into a solid national unit. On June 12, 1776, almost a _MONTH_ before the Declaration of Independence was announced, a committee was appointed to draft the "Articles of Confederation."

Little did the Founders realize that it would be 11 years before they would know how to put together a sound constitution for a free, prosperous people. In 1776 they still had much to learn. As Thomas Jefferson wrote: "We had never been permitted to exercise self-government. When forced to assume it, we were novices in its science." (Saul K. Padover, *Thomas Jefferson on Democracy*, New York: The New American Library, Inc., 1939, p. 33.)

A country without a constitution.

I

A. The first draft of the Articles of Confederation was prepared under the direction of John Dickinson of Pennsylvania. Dickinson was a great patriot but had originally been opposed to _Independence_. It was only after King George III had rejected all of their petitions for conciliation and ordered vindictive reprisals against the colonies that Dickinson saw that separation was inevitable. However, in his original draft he provided for a central government almost as _strong_ as the British crown. A shocked Congress received Dickinson's draft on July 12, just eight days after they had declared their independence from such a government.

B. Sixteen months of prolonged debate resulted in a new draft, which was adopted by Congress on November 15, 1777. This draft left the central government extremely _weak_ and the states vigorously independent. The weaknesses of the Articles of Confederation almost caused the United States to lose the Revolutionary War. It provided for:

1. No _executive_.
2. No federal _judicial_ system.
3. No power to _tax_.
4. No power to _enforce_ its decrees. (In other words, the national government simply had to depend upon the cooperation of the states.)

John Dickinson

C. Congress had not yet found the balanced center of the political spectrum which Jefferson said was so essential. The Articles of Confederation were too close to ___ANARCHY___.

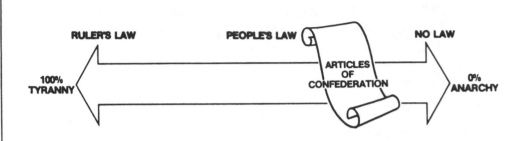

RULER'S LAW   PEOPLE'S LAW   NO LAW

ARTICLES OF CONFEDERATION

100% TYRANNY   0% ANARCHY

D. In spite of its weaknesses, the Articles of Confederation contained many valuable principles. In fact, more than ___50___ major provisions in the Articles were later included in the Constitution of 1787.

E. The ratification of the Articles of Confederation was delayed until the smaller states, particularly Maryland, induced the larger states to surrender to ___Congress___ their claims to western lands. The Articles finally went into full force and effect on March 1, 1781, although for all intents and purposes Congress had been functioning under them for more than four years.

II | Having declared their independence from Britain, the Americans then had to sustain it by force of arms. The eight-year Revolutionary War turned out to be a ___frustrating___ war.

A. The Americans were caught without a well-structured system of strong central government to run the war.

B. They were facing the most powerful empire on earth, with the largest army and the most powerful navy in the world.

C. They had no trained ___Army___ and no ___Navy___ whatsoever.

D. The central government had no money with which to finance the war.

E. There were strong loyalist or ___Tory___ elements throughout the country who were bitterly opposed to independence and actually fought with the British.

F. The assistance of ___France___ in providing supplies was highly significant, but the impact of her troops and naval support was extremely disappointing. The brilliant exception was the victory at Yorktown.

G. In summary, it could be accurately stated that financially, politically, administratively, militarily, and logistically, the United States should have ___lost___ the war.

There were many heroes in the Revolutionary War, but for sheer grit and steel-girded fortitude, none exceeded _George_ _Washington_.

III

A. At no time was he completely and wholeheartedly supported by either the Congress or the _States_.

B. Throughout most of the war he was being secretly maligned in Congress by his two jealous subordinates, General Charles Lee and General Horatio Gates, each of whom had been former _British_ officers and wanted to replace him as commander in chief. Lee turned out to be a traitor and Gates a coward.

C. Washington won most of his battles with men who were starving, freezing, poorly clothed, poorly equipped, half-trained, and often ill.

D. After any battle which proved less than victorious, his army would melt

George Washington

away except for two or three thousand stalwarts, and a new army would have to be recruited for the next encounter.

E. At the end of the war, some military and financial leaders of the nation wanted to place Washington in power as ___king___ George I of America. He turned away from the proffered honor in total disdain and retired to his farm in Virginia.

IV

The battles of the Revolutionary War tell the story. Washington and his ragtag army fought a cruel and bitter conflict for eight years on the razor's edge of imminent and foreboding _____. Truly, it was a miracle war.

Battle	Date	Winner
Boston	March 17, 1776	A
Charleston	June 28, 1776	A
New York	August 26, 1776	B
Trenton	December 26, 1776	
Princeton	December 27, 1776	
Ticonderoga	July 4, 1777	
Bennington	August 15, 1777	
Freemen's Farm	September 19, 1777	
Saratoga	October 17, 1777	
Brandywine	September 11, 1777	
Germantown	October 3, 1777	
Monmouth	June 28, 1778	
Savannah	December 29, 1778	
Vincennes	February, 1779	
Savannah	October 3, 1779	
Charleston	May 12, 1780	
Camden	August 15, 1780	
King's Mountain	October 7, 1780	
Cowpens	January 17, 1781	
Guilford Courthouse	March 15, 1781	
Yorktown	October 9, 1781	

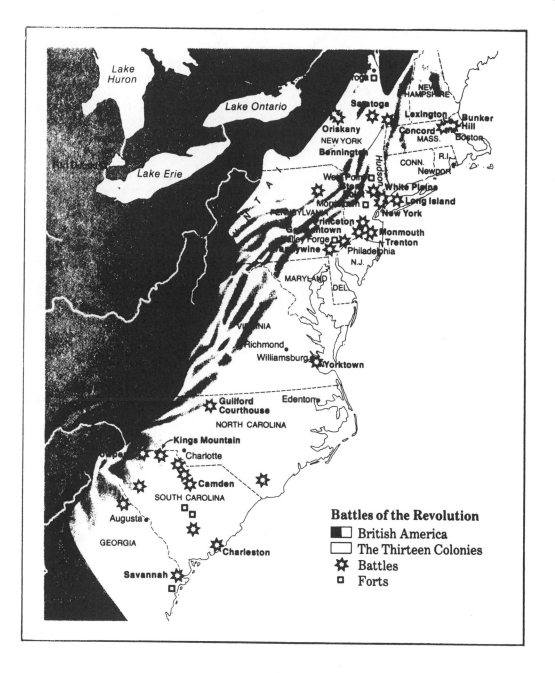

Battles of the Revolution

- ◨ British America
- ☐ The Thirteen Colonies
- ✦ Battles
- ◻ Forts

5

The Miracle at Philadelphia

Introduction

When the Founding Fathers assembled in Philadelphia on May 25, 1787, it was a
frightening experience. The entire American experiment was falling
to pieces:

A. The _unity_ that existed during the Revolutionary War had
disappeared.

B. There was a deep _depression_, with runaway inflation and rioting
in some places.

C. The states were _quarreling_ over boundaries in the west and
fishing rights in the east.

D. The states actually treated one another as _foreign_ countries,
charging customs on imports and exports.

E. Spain was threatening to seize territory along the _Mississippi
River_.

F. England would not remove her _troops_ from the northern border of
the United States.

G. Such _hostility_ had developed among the states that New
England was threatening to secede from the Union!

H. It was obvious the Articles of Confederation were a _failure_ and the
central government was completely incapable of dealing with all these
crises.

The whole civilized world was watching to see if the men assembled in
Philadelphia could save the dis-United States.

I It was almost a _miracle_ that the Constitutional Convention ever took
place.

A. None of the states seemed to want it. From all appearances, they each
seemed prepared to go their separate ways.

B. In 1783, after Washington learned that the army was planning to seize
power and try to make him king, he wrote to every state pleading with them
to hold a convention at the earliest possible date. _Nothing_ came of it.

C. On March 28, 1785, Washington invited delegates from his own state of
Virginia to meet with delegates from Maryland and work out a settlement of

their quarrel over trade and fishing rights. It was so successful that Congress was urged to hold a ___trade___ conference for all the states.

D. The trade conference was held at Annapolis in September 1786. A good spirit prevailed among the delegates, but since only ___5___ states were represented, there was not a quorum to do business. Nevertheless, the delegates decided to ask Congress to call a general convention so that the states could work out all their problems, both economic and political.

E. Congress finally scheduled a convention to meet on May 14, 1787.

II

The Constitutional Convention became the most important convocation of political leaders in the history of the world.

A. It was fortunate that each of the states sent some of its most outstanding leaders to the convention.

B. Altogether, 73 delegates were appointed to attend the convention. Unfortunately, however, many of the states provided no expense money for their representatives, and as a result, only ___55___ actually participated. Many of these, including James Madison, had to borrow money to attend.

C. The only state that did not send any representatives was Rhode Island. Its leaders said they wanted to remain independent of the other states and had no intention of consenting to a stronger central government. The other states began calling her "___rogue___ Island." Thirteen businessmen from Rhode Island wrote a letter to the convention apologizing for the behavior of their leaders.

D. Because of personal circumstances, George Washington was almost unable to attend. His brother had recently died, his mother and sister were seriously ill, and Washington was in such pain from rheumatism that he could not sleep at night. Nonetheless, his friends persuaded him to attend, since otherwise the convention would have failed.

E. Benjamin Franklin was ___81___ years old and had difficulty attending, even though Philadelphia was his home. Four trusties from the local prison carried him in a sedan chair to and from the convention each day.

Benjamin Franklin

Thomas Jefferson

John Adams

F. Two men who made some of the greatest contributions to the convention were unable to attend:

1. _John Adams_ was serving as the American minister to England. Nevertheless, he had written a treatise entitled *A Defense of the Constitutions of Government of the United States,* and this document was widely read by delegates to the convention.

2. _Thomas Jefferson_ was also absent serving as the American minister to France. However, he had sent more than a hundred carefully selected books to James Madison, and Madison made himself a walking encyclopedia on the history and political philosophy of governments of the past. Jefferson corresponded with him on what he considered to be the essential elements of a good constitution. Therefore, a month before the convention, Madison wrote a summary of the weaknesses of the Articles of Confederation entitled "The Vices of the Political System of the United States." He then outlined the kind of constitution he thought would remedy the situation. No one came to the convention better prepared than James Madison.

G. James Madison was _8_ years younger than Thomas Jefferson. He was short and slight of stature and in his early years had been quite sickly. He attended Princeton, where he came under the intensive discipline of John Witherspoon, who later signed the Declaration of Independence.

James Madison

Madison had worked closely with Jefferson in Virginia, helping him develop his massive legislative reform and pushing some of it through after Jefferson left for France. Madison served in Congress from 1780 to 1783 and was considered the most __able__ political leader in the national assembly.

It was fortunate that Madison was present to provide the principal leadership at the Constitutional Convention, where he represented the advanced views of both himself and Jefferson.

III The opening of the convention had to be postponed because the delegates from only two states had arrived by May 14, 1787. This turned out to be a great __advantage__.

1. When the Virginia delegation saw that there would be a delay, the members immediately began holding early-morning planning sessions where __Madison__ outlined the results of his research. He recommended a structure of government completely different from that of the Articles of Confederation.

2. By the time a quorum (or majority) of the state delegations arrived in Philadelphia, the Virginia delegation had formulated __15__ resolutions describing some of the things they thought the new system of government should contain. These became known as Virginia's "Fifteen Resolves," which constituted the basic agenda for the convention when it finally assembled. Other resolutions were added as the convention got under way.

IV The Constitutional Convention officially opened on Friday, May 25, 1787. By this time the delegations from seven states had arrived. Others came along in due time until all the states were represented except __Rhode Island__.

Independence Hall, Philadelphia

A. The first order of business was to elect a president of the convention. ~~James~~ ~~Madison~~ *Geo. Washington* was elected unanimously.

B. A secretary named Major William Jackson of South Carolina had been employed, but he was not really competent. It was *James Madison* who was the real secretary and historian. He sat in front and took copious notes on everything that was said. After each session, Madison would work far into the night filling in details. He occasionally made himself ill from fatigue and overwork trying to capture every detail of the convention. These notes were kept secret for *50* years, but they were finally published by an act of Congress in 1843. They constitute the most authoritative record available on the convention.

C. The convention followed a procedure that greatly facilitated informal debate of each issue. For purposes of discussion, the convention would resolve itself into a "Committee of the *whole*," consisting of all the convention delegates. This would permit them to reach temporary decisions not counted as the official position of the convention. This is why we find Washington stepping down from the chair several times during the convention and having Nathaniel Gorham of Massachusetts take his place as chairman of the Committee of the Whole. Once they had reached an agreement, they would turn themselves back into a convention and vote formally on the question.

Before the convention was over, the members had reached general agreement on all the major issues except three:

1. How soon the national government should begin to regulate or abolish <u>slavery</u>.

2. Whether votes in Congress should be according to individual states or the <u>populations</u> of the states.

3. Whether the federal government should have authority to regulate interstate <u>commerce</u>.

Since these are the only real compromises in the Constitution, it is a mistake for textbooks to describe the Constitution as a "conglomerate of compromises." On all other issues the Founders "talked it out" until they had reached general agreement or near consensus.

D. It was Tuesday, May 29, after the delegations from nine states had arrived and all the preliminaries had been arranged, that Governor Edmund Randolph of Virginia arose and introduced the 15 <u>resolutions</u>, or "resolves" which the Virginia delegation had prepared in advance. These became the agenda for the convention from that point on.

E. Since no country in the world had ever been structured the way the Virginia Resolves suggested, every single point had to be carefully analyzed and debated.

1. It should be kept in mind that Congress had told the delegates that they were meeting for the "sole and express purpose of <u>amending</u> the Articles of Confederation." However, there was a general feeling that a completely different kind of constitutional structure was needed.

2. The delegates knew that whatever they proposed would have to be approved by <u>Congress</u> and the states, so they felt justified in proposing a completely new constitution rather than putting patches on the defective Articles of Confederation.

3. It took the convention <u>4</u> months to reach final agreement on the many prickly issues raised by the Virginia Resolves and write them into a formal constitution.

Edmund Randolph

V

Highlights of the Constitutional Convention:

A. From May 30 to June 13, the convention discussed the 15 Virginia Resolves one at a time. They first determined points of general agreement and postponed until a later date the questions involving extensive debate.

B. On June 14, William Paterson of New Jersey asked to have the day free for the preparation of a new plan that the <u>smaller</u> states wished to present the following day.

C. The New Jersey Plan was laid before the convention on Friday, June 15. Before presenting this plan, Paterson said that the smaller states wanted to scrap the Virginia Resolves and go back to patching up the original Articles of Confederation.

D. The following day, James Wilson of Pennsylvania compared the Virginia Plan and the New Jersey Plan point by point:

	Virginia Plan	New Jersey Plan
Legislature	Two branches	Single body
Source of legislative power	The people	The states
Executive	One	More than one
Legislative action	By a majority	By a small minority
Extent of legislative power	All national concerns	Limited objects
Remove executive	By impeachment	Upon application of majority of states

E. While the convention was contemplating the two different plans, Alexander ___Hamilton___ arose and presented an entirely different plan of his own. He said it was too dangerous to tread untried waters. It would be best to go back to the British pattern. According to his recommendations:

1. A single executive would be chosen for ___life___ by electors from the states. He wanted the president to have an absolute veto over any legislation, similar to the veto power of the king of England.

2. Senators would also be chosen for ___life___, as was the case in the English House of Lords.

William Paterson

James Wilson

Alexander Hamilton

3. Members of the House of Representatives would be chosen by the people for a term of ___3___ years.

4. Governors of the states would be appointed by the _Federal_ government, just as the king of England had appointed colonial governors before the Revolutionary War.

Hamilton's plan was "approved by all and supported by _None_." It was not even discussed, let alone voted upon.

F. On June 19, a moving speech was given by James _Madison_, in which he said that the convention must come up with a "Constitution for the Ages," and that only the Virginia Plan would stand the test of time. Immediately afterward, the New Jersey Plan was voted down and Hamilton's plan was also abandoned. Hamilton even abandoned it himself and returned to New York soon afterward. However, he came back before the convention adjourned.

G. After June 19, the convention tried to probe some of the more prickly questions which had previously been postponed. The next five weeks (through July 26) are known as the _Crisis_ period of the convention.

H. Just trying to decide how the President should be elected required more than ___60___ ballots between July 10 and 16. It was during this dark period that Washington wrote:

"I almost despair of seeing a favorable issue to the proceedings of the Convention, and do therefore repent having had any agency in the business." (John C. Fitzpatrick, ed., *The Writings of George Washington,* 39 vols., Washington: United States Government Printing Office, 1931–44, 29:409.)

Observers said he looked as grim as when he was at Valley Forge.

It was during the quarreling and heated debating on June 28 that 81-year-old Benjamin Franklin made his famous plea for prayer.

On July 10 the two remaining delegates from New York, Lansing and Yates, left the convention and never returned.

I. A breakthrough came on July 16, when the delegates were at last able to agree on a formula for allocating _representation_ in Congress.

1. The small states had been determined to have _one_ vote for each state as provided in the Articles of Confederation.

2. The larger states had insisted that representation should be according to _Population_. Delegates from Georgia argued that this would give the big state of Virginia 16 times more representatives than Georgia. Madison argued back that if each state had one vote, then a person from Georgia would have 16 times more representation than a citizen of Virginia.

3. Both sides finally agreed to accept the suggestion of Roger Sherman of

Benjamin Franklin urged that the Convention open each day with prayer.

Connecticut that each state have ___equal___ representation in the Senate but that seats in the House of Representatives should be apportioned to the states according to population. This suggestion was made three separate times during the heated debates before it was finally accepted.

J. Finally, by July 26, the principal issues had been sufficiently settled to put the Constitution into rough form. A Committee on ___detail___ was therefore appointed, with instruction to have its report completed by August 6.

K. From August 6 to September 8, the convention hammered out many more important details which needed refining. By this time, ___4___ of the 55 delegates had departed and gone home. Hamilton, Yates, and Lansing of New York were among those who left. Later Hamilton returned, but he could not vote because his state did not have the required number of delegates for a vote.

L. On September 8, the amended rough draft from the Committee on Detail was turned over to a special Committee on ___Style___ for the final rewrite. Most of the rewrite was done in four days by a highly skilled lawyer and writer who was a delegate from Pennsylvania. His name was Gouverneur ___Morris___.

VI

Unveiling the Founders' great new success formula for freedom and prosperity.

A. The power base was structured exactly as it had been visualized from reading the history of ancient Israel and the Anglo-Saxons. It was fixed firmly in the balanced ___Center___ of the political spectrum.

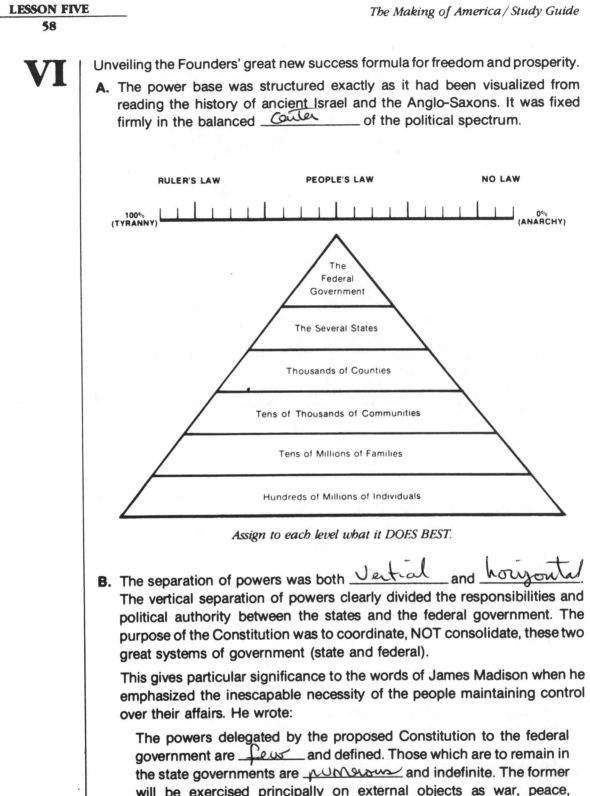

Assign to each level what it DOES BEST.

B. The separation of powers was both ___Vertical___ and ___horizontal___. The vertical separation of powers clearly divided the responsibilities and political authority between the states and the federal government. The purpose of the Constitution was to coordinate, NOT consolidate, these two great systems of government (state and federal).

This gives particular significance to the words of James Madison when he emphasized the inescapable necessity of the people maintaining control over their affairs. He wrote:

> The powers delegated by the proposed Constitution to the federal government are ___few___ and defined. Those which are to remain in the state governments are ___numerous___ and indefinite. The former will be exercised principally on external objects as war, peace, negotiation, and foreign commerce; with which last the power of taxation will, for the most part, be connected. The powers reserved to the several states will extend to all the objects which, in the ordinary course of affairs, concern the lives, liberties and prosperity of the state. (*Federalist Papers*, No. 45.)

C. The Founders provided a _horizontal_____ separation of powers among the three major branches of government—the legislature, the executive, and the judiciary. This was later copied by all of the states. It was like creating a three-headed eagle with a common neck, so that each department would be independent but could not function without the support of the other two. In other words, it was separation of power with checks to keep everything in balance, as the following illustration demonstrates:

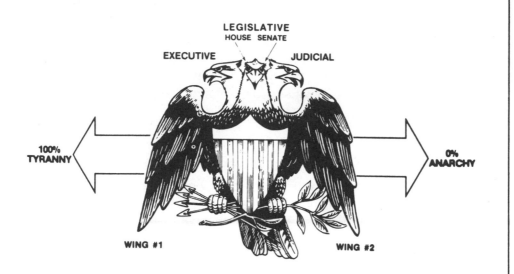

D. Each of the two wings is essential to keep the American eagle in the balanced _center_____ of the political spectrum.

1. Wing No. 1 might be referred to as the problem-solving wing or the wing of compassion. Those who function through this dimension of the system are sensitive to the unfulfilled needs of the people. They dream of elaborate plans to solve these problems.

2. Wing No. 2 has the responsibility of conserving the nation's resources and the people's freedom. Its function is to analyze the programs of Wing No. 1 with two questions. First, can we afford it? Second, what will it do to the rights and individual freedom of the people?

3. If either of these wings fails to perform its job, the American eagle will drift toward anarchy or tyranny. For example, if Wing No. 1 becomes infatuated with the idea of solving all the problems of the nation regardless of the cost, and Wing No. 2 fails to bring its power into play to sober the problem-solvers with a more realistic approach, the eagle will spin off toward the left, which is tyranny. On the other hand, if Wing No. 1 fails to see the problems that need solving and Wing No. 2 refuses to solve problems in an effort to save money, or to preserve the status quo, then the machinery of government loses its credibility and the eagle drifts toward the right, where the people decide to take matters into their own

hands. This can eventually disintegrate into anarchy, with a deep credibility gap developing between the people and their government.

4. However, if both of these wings fulfill their assigned functions, the American eagle can fly straighter and higher than any civilization in the history of the world. This is what the Founders envisioned as they finally concluded the Constitutional Convention.

VII

On Monday, September 17, 1787, ___41___ out of the original 55 delegates solemnly met in the east room of Independence Hall for the signing.

A. Because a few delegates still had some significant reservations, Franklin asked that the Constitution be signed by the majority of each delegation so they could say it was by "unanimous consent" of all the "states" represented. This was done. Three delegates did not sign:

1. Elbridge Gerry of Massachusetts

2. George Mason of Virginia

3. Governor Edmund Randolph of Virginia

Their main objection was that the Constitution did not include a ___Bill___ of ___Rights___.

B. As the delegates were signing, James Madison carefully watched each of them. When Franklin signed, Madison wrote: "The old man ___wept___." (Catherine Drinker Bower, *Miracle at Philadelphia*, London: Hamish Hamilton, 1967, p. 213.)

C. As the last delegates were signing, Franklin referred to a picture of the sun on the back of George Washington's chair. He said: "I have...often, in the course of the session,...looked at that [sun] behind the president without being able to tell whether it was rising or setting. But now at length I have the happiness to know that it is a rising and not a setting sun." (Max Farrand, ed., *The Records of the Federal Convention of 1787,* 4 vols., New Haven, Conn.: Yale University Press, 1937, 2:648.)

"It is a rising and not a setting sun."—Benjamin Franklin

Conclusion

As the famous convention came to a close, it was as though a great battle had been won. But the Constitution still had to go to the Congress and the people. This meant that the great intellectual battle to get the American charter of liberty established in the hearts and minds of the American people still had to be fought. Their carefully structured formula for freedom and prosperity was about to go through its "baptism of fire."

6

The Founders' Formula

Introduction

There are many Americans who have resided in the United States all their lives, yet do not have the slightest idea how the Founders arrived at the formula for constitutional government that has made America such a success.

When these people are elected into office, they are usually well-meaning and patriotic, but they lack the Founders' wisdom. They have never had an opportunity to study the Founders' political philosophy or their concept of prosperity economics.

The next seven lessons will cover the highlights of the Founders' formula for a free and prosperous America. If any particular point seems obscure, see the more comprehensive discussion in *The Making of America*. In that text the material is presented in the same order as it is in this study outline.

I

The Constitution goes to Congress and then to the people.

A. On September 17, 1787, the Constitution was signed and sent to Congress in ___New York___ under a cover letter written by George Washington.

B. James Madison and others who had helped write the Constitution were members of Congress, and they enthusiastically explained the new American charter to their colleagues.

C. After only ___8___ days of hearings, Congress approved the Constitution and sent it to the states without any changes.

D. Each state was invited to call a special convention of delegates selected by the people to ratify the Constitution and thereby make it a manifesto of the ___people___.

E. Several states barely made it into the Union:

   1. In Massachusetts, if ___10___ delegates had changed their votes, that state would have been left out of the Union.

   2. In New Hampshire, ___6___ votes the other way would have been fatal.

   3. In Virginia, ___4___ votes the other way would have been fatal.

   4. In New York, ___2___ votes the other way would have been fatal.

   5. In Rhode Island, ___1___ votes the other way would have been fatal.

How would *you* have reacted to this strange new document? We will now go through it phrase by phrase.

II   The Preamble to the Constitution

A. Gouverneur Morris set forth the six main purposes of good government for the first time in political history when he wrote the Preamble:

We the people of the United States, in order to form a more perfect _Union_, establish _justice_, insure domestic _Tranquility_, provide for the common _defense_, promote the general _welfare_, and secure the blessings of _Liberty_ to ourselves and our posterity, do ordain and establish this Constitution for the United States of America.

B. The Preamble is a wonderfully succinct introduction to the content of the Constitution, and every American should learn it by heart. It is easy to memorize by using sign language while reciting it. (See Appendix, page 131.)

III   Article I: The Legislature

One of the most important provisions of the Constitution is Article I, Section 1, which reads:

All legislative powers herein granted shall be vested in a _Congress_ of the United States, which shall consist of a Senate and House of Representatives.

A. This gave the people the right *not* to be subject to any federal law unless it has been reviewed and approved by a majority of the people's representatives.

B. Gradually the executive and judicial branches of the government began to usurp this authority in the following ways:

1. The executive branch began making laws by issuing "executive _orders_" and publishing them as new laws in the *Federal Register*.

2. The President was authorized to set up certain types of regulatory agencies. These bodies immediately began issuing thousands of orders that were treated as "laws" which could be enforced in the courts. This kind of regulation is called _administrative_ law.

3. The President also began to involve the nation in many new legal obligations with foreign powers by entering into extensive and sometimes secret _executive_ agreements. According to the Constitution, foreign commitments should be handled through treaties approved by the _Senate_.

4. The Supreme Court has also created numerous new laws under the guise of merely interpreting old ones. This was particularly true during the administration of Chief Justice Earl Warren from 1954 to 1969. This is called _judicial_ legislation.

Article I, Section 2: The Structure of the House of Representatives.

A. Representatives are elected every _2_ years, and the states are to decide what qualifications a person must have to vote for a Representative. Whoever can vote for a representative in the state legislature can vote for a Representative in Congress.

B. To be a member of the House, a person must be (by the time he is sworn in): age _25_, a citizen _7_ years, and an inhabitant of the state he represents.

C. A census must be taken every ten years, with Representatives being apportioned among the states according to their population. The Founders did not want too many Representatives, so they determined that each one must represent at least _30,000_ people. By 1929, the House had grown to 435 members, and a law was therefore passed which stipulated that the number could not be increased beyond 435. Of course, our population has greatly increased, and therefore today each Congressman represents approximately _500,000_ people.

D. If a Representative resigns or dies, the _governor_ of that state must arrange for a new election.

E. The House is authorized to choose its Speaker as well as any other officers that are needed.

F. Only the House can initiate impeachment proceedings against officers in the other branches of government. In Congress, obnoxious members are not impeached but are _expelled_ by a two-thirds vote.

IV

V **Article I, Section 3:** The Structure of the Senate.

A. It is in the Senate that all of the states, regardless of their size or population, are equal in representation. Each state has ___2___ Senators who serve for terms of ___6___ years, and each Senator has one vote.

B. Because both the Presidency and the House of Representatives could undergo a complete turnover at the same election, it was provided that only ___1/3___ of the Senate would be elected every two years, thereby leaving at least two-thirds of the Senate intact in order to maintain a continuity in government affairs.

C. To qualify as a candidate for the Senate, a person must (at the time he is sworn in) be ___30___ years of age. He must have been a citizen for ___9___ years and must be an inhabitant of the state he represents.

D. The Senate does not get to choose its presiding officer, who is always the ___Vice President___. But if he is absent for any reason, the Senate can appoint one of its own members to preside until he returns. The Senate can also appoint any additional officers or staff as they are needed.

E. We do not ordinarily think of the Senate as a judicial body, but just as the House has the exclusive responsibility of bringing charges against government officials for the purpose of impeachment, the Senate has the exclusive responsibility of determining guilt. If the President is impeached, the ___Chief Justice___ must preside over the hearing; otherwise, the President's own running mate would be presiding over his impeachment proceedings—clearly an unacceptable conflict of interest.

VI **Article I, Section 4:** Congressional Elections and the Requirement that Congress Convene Once Each Year.

A. It is interesting that the "times, places and manner" of electing Senators and Representatives was left up to the states, but there was a provision that Congress could alter the arrangements if necessary. No such steps were

Casting paper ballots in the general election, 1860.

taken by Congress until 1842, when the states were required to elect their Representatives from specific _districts_ instead of electing them "at large." The next intervention was in 1866, when all of the states were required to hold elections on the first Tuesday after the first Monday in November. Since then, most federal laws dealing with elections have been directed against fraud or corrupting the political process.

B. Congress does not have to wait to be called into session by the President, but is under mandate to assemble on a specific date each year. It was originally the first Monday in December, so that there would be sufficient time to prepare for the President's inauguration on March 4. The Twentieth Amendment changed it to January _3_ and the President's inauguration to January _20_.

Article I, Section 5: The Internal Operations of Congress.

A. Both houses of Congress determine whether or not their members possess the required qualifications and whether or not they have been legally _elected_. The courts cannot decide such cases.

B. Neither house can do business until a _quorum_ is present consisting of "a majority" (one-half plus one), but a minority can vote to punish the absentees in order to compel a majority to attend.

C. Each of the houses of Congress is self-sufficient and self-contained. Each is authorized to:

1. Make rules and set up proceedings for conducting its business.

2. Punish its members for misbehavior.

3. Expel a member when _2/3_ of that particular house concur in the action.

D. Each house is to keep a record of all its proceedings and publish them unless certain parts must be kept _Secret_ because it is in the public interest to do so.

E. Ordinarily decisions are made by voice vote—"yea" or "nay." However, if _1/5_ of those present desire a recorded vote, it must be done.

F. Congress must continue in session until both houses agree on a time of adjournment. As we shall see later, if they cannot agree, the President has the power to adjourn them (although this has never been done). During a session, either house may take a temporary adjournment—but never for more than _3_ days, and it cannot decide to reconvene at some other place unless the other house agrees.

Article I, Section 6: The Sticky Problem of Compensation for Congressmen and Doubling Up on Government Jobs.

A. A number of the delegates who were supposed to participate in the Constitutional Convention could not come because their states would not

VII

Congress in session.

VIII

provide expenses or compensation during the four months the Convention was in session. The Founders, therefore, decided that members of the House and Senate would be paid out of the U.S. treasury. As of 1983 they were paid $60,663 annually, plus fringe benefits and federal retirement payments after a certain time. They are also allowed to set their own salaries—a provision Madison thought was "indecent."

B. To protect Congressmen in carrying out their duties, they cannot be arrested en route to or from a session of Congress nor during the time they are there unless the offense is _treason_, or _felony_, or breach of the peace.

C. Senators and Congressmen also have complete freedom of speech while speaking or debating in Congress and cannot be questioned in any other place for what they say (such as being charged with _slander_). This privilege is sometimes abused, but it was felt to be necessary in order to ensure complete freedom of debate.

D. Those elected to Congress cannot afterwards hold any position in the government which was created or for which the pay was _increased_ while they were in Congress. Neither can a member of Congress be appointed to any government job while he is serving as a representative of his state.

IX

Article I, Section 7: The Procedure for the Passing of Laws.

A. Originally, Senators represented their states rather than the populace of their states. Therefore, all bills involving the appropriation of funds had to be initiated in the House of Representatives, whose members are spokesmen for the taxpayers of their states. This is still the rule, even though Senators today (by virtue of the Seventeenth Amendment) are also elected by the people of their states rather than being appointed by their state legislatures as the Founders originally designed it. Once a bill has been passed by the House, the Senate can offer _amendment_ if it desires.

B. When a bill is introduced, it is simply given a number and sent to the appropriate committee. There it _dies_ unless the person introducing it has sufficient support to get the bill brought before the committee for a hearing. If the committee sends it to the floor for discussion or the house in question votes it out of the committee, the bill is then publicly discussed, amended, and finally voted upon. If approved, it must then go to the other house, where it may die or be approved. If the other house amends the bill, it has to go back to the original house for approval of the modified version. The bill cannot go to the President until both houses have approved the identical measure.

C. When a bill arrives on the desk of the President, he has _10_ days to consider it. If he takes no action on it, the bill automatically becomes law. If he objects to any part of it, he can send it back to Congress, and it cannot

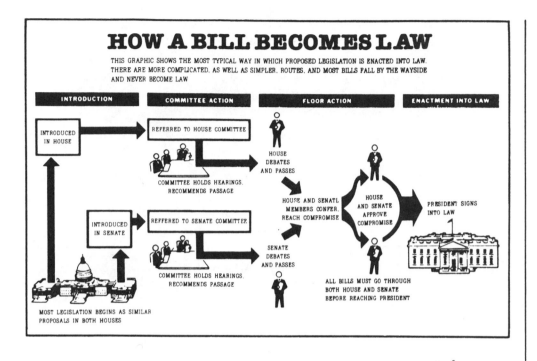

HOW A BILL BECOMES LAW

THIS GRAPHIC SHOWS THE MOST TYPICAL WAY IN WHICH PROPOSED LEGISLATION IS ENACTED INTO LAW.
THERE ARE MORE COMPLICATED, AS WELL AS SIMPLER, ROUTES, AND MOST BILLS FALL BY THE WAYSIDE
AND NEVER BECOME LAW

| INTRODUCTION | COMMITTEE ACTION | FLOOR ACTION | ENACTMENT INTO LAW |

INTRODUCED IN HOUSE

REFERRED TO HOUSE COMMITTEE

COMMITTEE HOLDS HEARINGS, RECOMMENDS PASSAGE

HOUSE DEBATES AND PASSES

HOUSE AND SENATE MEMBERS CONFER, REACH COMPROMISE

HOUSE AND SENATE APPROVE COMPROMISE

PRESIDENT SIGNS INTO LAW

INTRODUCED IN SENATE

REFFERED TO SENATE COMMITTEE

COMMITTEE HOLDS HEARINGS, RECOMMENDS PASSAGE

SENATE DEBATES AND PASSES

ALL BILLS MUST GO THROUGH BOTH HOUSE AND SENATE BEFORE REACHING PRESIDENT

MOST LEGISLATION BEGINS AS SIMILAR PROPOSALS IN BOTH HOUSES

become law unless they satisfy the President's objections or ___2/3___ of both houses override the President's veto.

If Congress passes numerous bills just before adjournment and dumps them on the President's desk so that he does not have 10 days to consider them, none of them will become law without his signature. He may leave the rest in his pocket, so to speak, where they die. This is called the President's ___pocket___ veto.

Conclusion

And so we come to the conclusion of Article I dealing with the Preamble and the organization and structure of Congress. Our next lesson is one of the most controversial parts of the entire Constitution. It is entitled "The States Delegate Twenty Powers to Congress" and begins with the famous Section 8 of Article I, in which the states finally decide to trust the federal government with 20 areas of power.

7

The States Delegate
18 Twenty Powers to Congress

Introduction

In 1776, the states had refused to delegate enough authority to Congress to enable it to perform its legitimate functions. As a result they almost lost the Revolutionary War. In lessons 7 and 8 we shall discover which powers the states were willing to delegate to the federal government.

Article I, Section 8, Clause 1: "The Congress shall have power to lay and collect taxes...to pay the debts and provide for the common defense and general welfare of the United States; but all duties, imposts and excises shall be uniform throughout the United States."

I

A. Here are the principal types of taxes:

1. Poll tax.

2. Property tax.

3. Income tax.

4. Excise tax.

5. Sales tax.

6. Duties or imposts, sometimes called _tariffs_.

B. Congress can use taxes of various kinds to pay the _debts_ of the United States.

1. The Founders elected to assume responsibility for the payment of all debts accumulated during the Revolutionary War by both the national government and the _states_. This amounted to more than $79 million—a gigantic sum in those days.

2. This willingness to assume past debts did much to establish the credibility of the new government among foreign banks.

C. Congress can raise revenue to pay for the common _defense_ of the nation. Such a defense is not considered adequate unless it is sufficient to discourage an attack by potential enemies.

D. In connection with the taxing power, this clause states that revenues can only be expended for the _general welfare_ of the whole nation as it carries out the list of duties set forth. These funds are not to be spent for individuals, special groups, or particular geographical regions. This clause was designed by the Founders to be a ___Limitation___ on the taxing power of Congress. However:

1. When Alexander Hamilton became Secretary of the Treasury under Washington, he argued that this clause was a general ___grant___ of ___power___ which allowed Congress to tax and spend money for *any* good cause, regardless of whether it was among the enumerated powers, or whether it was for local or special welfare rather than general welfare. (He had never presented this idea at the Constitutional Convention, where it would have been immediately rejected because it torpedoed the whole idea of a ___limited___ government!)

2. Hamilton was immediately opposed by ___Jefferson___ and ___Madison___, who emphasized the original intent of the Founders in having the national government carry out its assignment in ways that would benefit the nation as a whole, not special groups or special regions.

3. The Founders' original intent generally prevailed until ___1936___, when the Supreme Court virtually amended the Constitution by a judicial opinion in the *Butler* case. Justice Roberts was joined by four other justices in handing down a dictum that thereafter Congress could follow Hamilton's doctrine of taxing and spending money for any cause it considered beneficial.

4. This unconstitutional dictum opened the floodgates of the U.S. treasury to virtually unlimited political looting, with the following results:

   a. Federal budgets rose from a little over $6 billion in 1936 to more than ___600 billion___ in 1980.

   b. Congressmen and Senators began campaigning on the basis of their success in concocting plans to bring more ___federal___ money into their respective states.

   c. Instead of limiting the federal government to the relatively few areas of responsibility outlined in the *Federalist Papers*, Congress began financing every "good cause" that offered an ___excuse___ for spending federal money in their states.

   d. President Lyndon Johnson openly announced that the idea was to take from the "___haves___" and give to the "___have-nots___." This is a program of "redistribution of wealth," which Samuel Adams said the Founders had tried to make unconstitutional.

   e. The Founders warned that the looting of one group of citizens for the benefit of another group is assigning to government a power which individual citizens do not have the ___authority___ to assign. They can only assign to government what they can rightfully do themselves, and looting one neighbor for the benefit of another would be considered a ___crime___.

5. Political and economic analysts such as Dr. Milton Friedman have pointed out that this deliberate smashing of the "chains" of the Constitution referred to by Jefferson is rapidly corrupting the whole American system in one generation.

   a. It has destroyed _equals_ protection of individual rights by selective taxing and selective regulation of business and industry.

   b. It destroys states' rights by allowing improper federal activities within the states on the ground that it brings in vast quantities of federal _funds_.

   c. It has greatly increased state taxes collected to provide _matching_ funds.

   d. It has created a nationwide climate of excessive taxation on all levels— to the point where the average citizen is funneling approximately _43_ percent of everything he earns into government programs.

   e. Reckless and profligate spending by government has produced a climate in which fraud, theft, and embezzlement of government funds has become almost routine. (The General Accounting Office listed these losses at more than _44 Billion_ as of 1978.)

   f. Unconstitutional federal funding has completely confused the role of strong, local _self_ - _goverment_. It has eroded the traditional sense of local responsibility and local restraint in spending.

E. Article I, Section 8, Clause 1, provides that taxes of various kinds shall be applied _Uniformly_ throughout the United States.

   1. The Supreme Court has interpreted this to mean geographical uniformity rather than a uniform assessment of individual citizens.

   2. Adoption of graduated income taxes was based on "ability to pay." If the rate were uniform, would the rich pay more than the poor? _Yes_.

   3. What basic constitutional right does a graduated income tax violate? _Equal_ protection of rights.

Article I, Section 8, Clause 2: Congress shall have power to "borrow money on the _Credit_ of the United States."

A. "Credit" is defined as "_trust_ in one's integrity in money matters and one's ability to fulfill financial obligations." There are two factors that seriously damage the credit of any government:

   1. Excessive _debt_

   2. Unstable currency due to _inflation_

   Let us briefly consider each of these:

B. Americans are currently facing a monumental burden in the form of a national _debt_ which exceeds the total debts of all other nations in the world combined!

II

1. The American national debt is now approaching a total of a ___trillion___ dollars. This is approximately $4,000 (as of 1980) for every man, woman, and child in the United States. The interest paid on this debt each year is more than the cost of World War I in real dollars.

2. What this really means is that by indulging in wild deficit spending each year, the present generation of Americans has been squandering almost a trillion dollars of the next generation's ___inheritance___. No other generation of Americans ever did this to its children before.

3. The Founders called this exploitation of the next generation ___immoral___. In a very real sense it is for the next generation "taxation without representation." As Jefferson said:

   We shall all consider ourselves unauthorized to saddle posterity with our debts, and morally bound to pay them ourselves; and consequently within what may be deemed the period of a generation, or the life [expectancy] of the majority." (Albert Ellery Bergh, ed., *The Writings of Thomas Jefferson,* 20 vols., Washington: Thomas Jefferson Memorial Association, 1907, 13:357.)

Thomas Jefferson

C. The credit of the United States can also be seriously damaged if it pays off its debts with money which has been cheapened by ___inflation___.

1. Inflation is defined as the "unnatural ___expansion___ of the money supply so that it reduces the buying power of money already in hand."

2. When the money supply grows only as fast as the production of goods and services there is a ___balance___, and the purchasing power of money remains stable from year to year. But when the government suddenly increases the money supply by borrowing or printing great quantitites of new paper money, it is unnatural and unbalancing.

3. Prices always rise to meet the approximate level of buyers' resistance; therefore, when there is much more money suddenly chasing after available goods and services, prices will automatically rise. These rising prices are not the ___cause___ of inflation, but the result of it.

4. Inflation not only destroys the credit of the nation but the economic ___security___ of the whole people.
   a. Savings ___shrink___.
   b. The value of insurance policies ___decreases___.
   c. Retired people often find themselves having to return to work in order to ___survive___.
   d. Farmers are caught in the squeeze between ___higher___ costs of equipment and labor and ___lower___ prices for their agricultural products during an inflationary period.
   e. Industrial workers find their paychecks buying less and less and therefore go on ___strike___.

5. The cause of inflation in the United States has been ___political___

rather than economic. As Dr. Milton Friedman emphasized repeatedly on his recent "Free to Choose" television series, politicians have been borrowing and printing tens of billions of dollars and using them to _____*buy*_____ votes. The unconstitutional *Butler* decision in 1936 made it all possible.

6. It is also a mere political device and power play when the government imposes price controls. It has devastating consequences _____*economically*_____:

    a. It leads to scarcity because price controls automatically wipe out the margin of _____*profit*_____.

    b. This leads to _____*black*_____ markets.

    c. And black markets always lead to _____*corruption.*_____.

Article I, Section 8, Clause 3: Congress shall have power to "regulate commerce with foreign nations, and among the several states, and with the Indian tribes."

III

A. *Foreign Commerce.* It has always been considered a plenary or inherent power in any sovereign government to regulate commerce and other relations with foreign powers. The regulation of foreign commerce is usually by:

1. Duties on imports to raise revenue.

2. Tariffs on certain foreign imports, with rates specifically designed to protect American workers and industries from the undermining of the U.S. market by goods produced by _____*cheap*_____ labor or slave labor.

3. The _____*inspection*_____ of certain types of imports to protect the American consumer from inferior products and to prevent the importation of foreign products that might carry destructive pests or infectious diseases.

4. The placing of an _____*embargo*_____ on goods from certain countries as a sanction (or protest) against hostility or the violation of international law.

B. *Interstate Commerce.* The regulation of interstate commerce has been one of the most distorted and abused provisions of the entire Constitution.

Interpretations of this clause have passed through several stages:

1. In the beginning, the whole thrust of this provision was to ensure the free _Flow_ of commerce among the several states, with emphasis on "commerce" rather than "regulation."

2. The power delegated by the states to the national government was intended to be limited to the regulation of _Transportation_, *not* the production or sale of goods and services going interstate.

3. Under the pressure of _war_ and _depression_, the Supreme Court twisted or reversed traditional cases on interestate commerce and introduced the unconstitutional doctrine that the federal government may regulate anything that affects interstate commerce, directly or _indirectly_.

4. This has resulted in usurpation of power in the form of sweeping federal regulations over:

   a. _Interstate_ transportation of goods.

   b. Labor _disputes_, which were formerly excluded from federal interference of any kind.

   c. _Price_ controls covering anything that affects interestate commerce directly or indirectly. These controls have been extended to everything from natural gas prices and distribution to the price of milk.

   d. _Federal_ controls on any industry involved directly or indirectly in the nationwide "current of commerce."

5. The only way to correct this obvious abuse of federal authority is by constitutional amendment. The following text is submitted for consideration:

   The regulation of interstate commerce shall be restricted to _transportation_ *and shall not apply to any phase of* _production_ *and sales or any activity which merely affects interstate commerce indirectly.*

C. The purpose of regulating commerce with the Indians was primarily to protect them from fraud and exploitation, particularly with reference to _alcohol_.

Article I, Section 8, Clause 4: Congress shall have the power to "establish a uniform rule of naturalization, and uniform laws on the subject of bankruptcies throughout the United States."

A. *Naturalization:*

1. Originally all of the states warmly _encouraged_ naturalization because of the shortage of manpower.

2. Regulations, such as they were, primarily fell to the individual states until the British refused to acknowledge the right of persons born in England to terminate their responsibilities to Britain and become American ___citizens___.

3. It became necessary for the federal government to intervene to prevent expatriated Englishmen from being physically removed from American ships. This was one of the primary causes of the War of 1812, and England did not officially allow her citizens to be expatriated until ___1870___.

B. *Bankruptcies:*

1. The first English bankruptcy law was passed in 1542 to prevent a debtor from defrauding his creditors by discriminating against them in favor of relatives or himself. His entire estate was seized under the ___involuntary___ bankruptcy statute.

2. The real problem arose later when the "debtor-relief laws'" allowed "honest" debtors who had become insolvent to take out ___voluntary___ bankruptcy. This facilitated the perpetration of fraud, and in the United States it was felt that a uniform federal law would provide the appropriate remedy.

3. The Federal Bankruptcy Act is still a plague to creditors. Abuses of the system became so rampant that a law was passed prohibiting any person from taking out bankruptcy any oftener than every ___6___ years!

8

Powers Delegated to Congress (continued)

I

Article I, Section 8, Clause 5: Congress shall have the power "to coin money, regulate the value thereof, and of foreign coin, and fix the standard of weights and measures."

A. The power to "coin money," as a constitutional directive, meant that the United States must always be on a _gold_ and _silver_ standard. In Section 10, we see that the states are forbidden to pay debts in anything but gold and silver. However:

1. The courts eventually allowed the government to print paper money to replace the "notes" being issued by thousands of banks. Even so, the courts originally ruled that government currency had to be redeemable in _gold_ or _silver_.

2. To "regulate the value thereof" originally referred to the value of coins, but in 1913 the management of American money and credit was turned over to a consortium of private banks called the Federal _Reserve_ System. This should have been considered unconstitutional, but the Supreme Court upheld it.

3. In 1933 the United States was taken off the domestic gold standard without a constitutional amendment. All gold had to be turned into the U.S. treasury except that used for jewelry, dentistry, or industry. In return for the gold, Americans received _silver_ certificates.

4. In 1964 the government went off the silver standard, and Federal _Reserve_ notes, which could no longer be redeemed in gold or silver, became legal tender.

5. In 1971 the government even refused to redeem with gold the paper dollars owned by _foreigners_. The American dollar immediately became a "floating" currency and has been dropping radically in buying power ever since.

B. The power of the federal government to "fix the standard of weights and measures" was to establish _uniformity_ and prevent _fraud_.

The shrinking dollar.

II

Article I, Section 8, Clause 6: Congress shall have the power "to provide for the punishment of _Counterfeiting_ the securities and current coin of the United States."

A. This was a widespread problem all during the 1800s. Enforcement of this law was assigned to the ___Secret Service___ branch of the U.S. Treasury Department.

B. Counterfeiting was made more difficult by the use of multicolored ___silk___ threads in the paper and the employment of extremely skilled engravers.

III

Article I, Section 8, Clause 7: Congress shall have the authority to "establish post offices and post roads."

A. Assigning the mails to the national government was intended to ensure ___Speed___ and ___security___.

B. Can the private sector handle the mail more economically? ___yes___. With equal security? ___no___. That is why the Post Office Department never subcontracts first-class mail as it does other types of mail.

C. The authority to establish "post roads" has been exercised merely to designate which existing roads will be used for the transport and delivery of the mails.

IV

Article I, Section 8, Clause 8: Congress was authorized to set up a national program to promote the arts and sciences by granting copyrights and patents.

A. The Founders did not believe an inventor or writer should be given a monopoly of his talent forever, but long enough to make it worthwhile so that he would be motivated to produce more.

B. The copyright law of 1909 allowed the author or artist a monopoly for 28 years subject to renewal for another 28. The 1978 law grants copyright for the ___lifetime___ of the writer or composer plus an additional ___50___ years.

C. A patent is good for ___17___ years. Must the applicant disclose all of the secrets of his invention to get a patent? ___yes___. Is this the reason some inventors never get a patent? ___yes___.

V

Article I, Section 8, Clause 9: Congress was authorized to set up a system of federal courts "inferior to the Supreme Court." This will be discussed in detail when we cover the judiciary in Article III.

Article I, Section 8, Clause 10: Congress was given the responsibility of punishing "piracies and felonies committed on the high seas, and offences against the law of nations."

A. All of these offenses are outside the jurisdiction of any ___state___.

B. They also involve relations with foreign powers, and therefore belong with the national government.

VI

Article I, Seciton 8, Clause 11: Congress, rather than the President, was given the responsibility of making all of the initial decisions concerning the waging of war.

A. Congress has the authority to ___declare___ war. Twice in our history, however, American troops were sent into major and lengthy combat situations (the Korean Conflict and the Vietnam War) *without* a declaration of war by Congress.

B. Congress can authorize the granting of "letters of marque and reprisal." Such a letter is an ___authorization___ to a private citizen allowing him to seize booty or make arrests as an official of the United States.

C. Congress has the responsibility of establish the ___rules___ dealing with captures on land or sea.

VII

Article I, Section 8, Clause 12: The authority of Congress to "raise and support armies" was restricted by the provision that no appropriations for this purpose should extend beyond ___2___ years. This was to prevent a President from building up a large standing army during peacetime and using it to seize and hold power permanently.

VIII

Article I, Section 8, Clause 13: Congress was empowered to "provide and maintain a ___Navy___."

IX

At the time of the Revolutionary War, the new nation had no navy, and John Paul Jones joined a number of other hearty souls to use private vessels operating under letters of marque and reprisal to fill the need. Clause 13 provided for the creation of a naval force under official government command.

X **Article I, Section 8, Clause 14:** Congress, not the President, should make the _____rules_____ and regulations for both the land and naval forces.

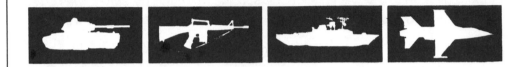

XI **Article I, Section 8, Clause 15:** Congress, rather than the President, was empowered to call up the _____militia_____ of the various states.

A. The Federal Code states that every _____male_____ 17 to 44 years of age is subject to call as a member of the militia of his state.

B. Congress can call up the militia for three purposes:
1. To suppress _____insurrections_____ (civil strife).
2. To repel an _____invasion_____ by a foreign power.
3. To execute the _____laws_____ of the United States.

XII **Article I, Section 8, Clause 16:** Congress has the responsibility of passing laws and appropriating money for the "organizing, arming, and disciplining" of the militia, so that these military support forces will be of _____uniform_____ quality throughout the states.

However, the Constitution gives the states the responsibility of carrying out the training and disciplining of their respective militia and appointing their own _____officers_____ to be in command. Only when a state militia is called up for active duty will federal military officers take over on the command level.

XIII **Article I, Section 8, Clause 17:** Congress was given exclusive authority over a ten-mile-square area to be designated the "Seat of the Government."

A. This was to prevent the area from being "politicalized" and subject to the kind of _____violence_____ which threatened Congress when it met in Philadelphia.

B. The deterioration of this protective provision began with adoption of the _____Twenty-Third_____ Amendment, which gave the District of Columbia three electoral votes in Presidential elections.

C. Another proposed amendment which would have given the District of Columbia (which is really the city of Washington, D.C.) the right to elect two

Washington, D.C.

Senators and one Congressman recently failed. The states refused to ratify this amendment because it would have wiped out the original intent of the Founders to keep the Seat of Government a neutral, nonpolitical territory.

D. The federal government was also authorized by the Constitution to occupy certain areas within a state if such areas were "purchased by the _consent_ of the [state] legislature."

1. The Constitution spelled out the purposes for which the federal government was authorized to make these purchases. Land could be purchased (with the consent of the state legislature):

   a. For the erection of _forts_.

   b. For magazines and _arsenals_.

   c. For _dock_ - _yards_.

   d. For other needful _buildings_ such as post offices.

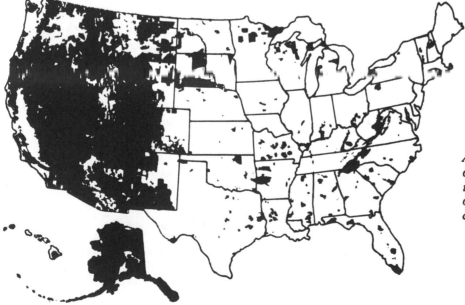

Areas darkened on this map are under federal ownership and control.

2. The first new state added to the Union was Ohio, which was admitted in 1803. Instead of giving the state all of the public lands, the federal government sold them to help pay off the national debt. Ownership was thereby "privatized" and immediatly went on the tax rolls of the state. This procedure was followed in all of the new states east of the Mississippi as well as all the new states in the Louisiana Purchase.

3. However, these provisions were completely ignored when the western states were admitted to the Union. The federal government unconstitutionally withheld vast sections of each state. In fact, when Alaska was admitted, 96 percent of the land was unconstitutionally withheld. The government still holds the following percentages of land in the western states:

Arizona	45%	Nevada	87%
California	45%	New Mexico	35%
Colorado	36%	Oregon	52%
Idaho	64%	Utah	66%
Montana	30%	Washington	30%

Compare this with Nebraska's 1 percent (one of the Louisiana Purchase states) or Massachusetts' 1 percent (one of the original 13 states).

XIV

Article I, Section 8, Clause 18: In order to carry out its responsibilities and exercise the powers granted to it, Congress was authorized to do whatever was _necessary_ and _proper_. This is called the "elastic clause" because it has sometimes been used to stretch federal power beyond its legitimate dimensions.

Section Nine

It is important to remember that the delegates to the Constitutional Convention were there to represent the interests of the states. Therefore, they undertook to restrict the national Congress in certain ways. This had never been done before. National legislatures (including England's Parliament) always considered themselves supreme and unrestricted in their law-making powers. Here are the areas in which the United States Congress was to be restrained by constitutional restrictions:

I

Article I, Section 9, Clause 1: Until _1808_, no restriction was to be placed on the importation or immigration of any persons (referring primarily to slaves, of course) which any of the states may consider proper. Furthermore, no federal tax on such persons was to exceed _$10_.

A. It was the consensus of the Convention that slavery was on its way out. Even in the South, only one out of _17_ white households owned slaves.

However, since slaves were considered "property," many of them were mortgaged to European banks. Emancipation of the slaves would have resulted in liens or foreclosures because of the loss of collateral by the European banks.

B. Three states (North Carolina, South Carolina, and Georgia) threatened to secede from the Union unless they were allowed twenty years to prepare for the phasing out of slavery. The other ten states decided that it was best to ensure the stability of the Union first and deal with the slavery question after the twenty-year period. Before agreeing to this, however, the northern states demanded that the southern states agree to give the federal government the power to regulate interstate commerce. The South agreed, and the matter was settled. These were two of the three main _compromises_ to be found in the Constitution.

Article I, Section 9, Clause 2: "The privilege of the writ of habeas corpus [an order of the court to have a prisoner brought before it; literally, "You have the body" brought before us] shall not be suspended" *except* when there is an _invasion_ or _insurrection_ and the public safety warrants it.

II

Article I, Section 9, Clause 3: Congress is absolutely forbidden to pass any bill of _attainder_ (an act of the legislature convicting a person of a crime without a _trial_ or a hearing). This clause also stipulates that Congress is forbidden to pass any *ex post facto* law, which makes an act a crime *after* the act occurred, or makes the offense more _serious_, or the penalty more _severe_, or deprives the individual of some _protection_.

III

Article I, Section 9, Clause 4: Congress was prohibited from assessing a head tax or other direct tax (such as an income tax) on the states unless it was uniformly assessed according to the _population_ of each state.

It was this restriction that made the Sixteenth Amendment necessary in order to tax on the basis of individual wealth instead of population.

IV

V **Article I, Section 9, Clause 5:** Congress is forbidden to put a ___tax___ or ___duty___ on any articles being exported from any state.

VI **Article I, Section 9, Clause 6:** Congress is forbidden to give ___preverence___ to one port over another or require the vessels of one state to enter or pay duties in the port of another state.

VII **Article I, Section 9, Clause 7:** No money shall be drawn from the treasury unless Congress has authorized it by an ___appropriation___, and a record of all receipts and expenditures shall be maintained and published.

VIII **Article I, Section 9, Clause 8:** No titles of ___nobility___ were to be granted to anybody within the United States, and no one holding public office was to accept any gift, title, or present from a foreign power without the consent of Congress.

Section Ten

The Founders also wanted to make it entirely clear that the states were under certain constitutional restrictions. There were two types: (1) things the states were *absolutely* forbidden to do, and (2) things the states were forbidden to do unless ___Congress___ consented.

I Here is what the states were *absolutely* forbidden to do under Article I, Section 10:

A. Enter into any ___treaty___, alliance, or confederation. (It was the last prohibition which became the crux of the Civil War.)

B. Grant letters of marque and reprisal (authorizing private citizens to make war on enemy ships, etc.).

C. ___coin___ money.

D. Emit bills of credit (paper money).

E. Use anything but ___gold___ and ___silver___ to pay debts. This proves that the gold standard was to be used by the entire nation, including the states.

F. Pass any bill of attainder (convicting a person of a crime by a legislative act without a trial or hearing).

G. Pass any *ex post facto* law (retroactive criminal statute).

H. Pass any law impairing contracts.

I. Grant any ___title___ of ___nobility___.

Here is what the states cannot do *unless* they get the permission of _Congress_ .

II

A. Impose duties on imports or exports except to cover the expense of making inspections. If there is any net profit, it goes to the U.S. _treasury_ .

B. Lay any duty on tonnage coming into a port.

C. Maintain troops or ships of war in time of _Peace_ .

D. Enter into any agreement or compact with another _state_ .

E. Engage in _war_ unless invaded or in such imminent danger that there is no time or opportunity to obtain the consent of Congress.

Conclusion

In lessons 7 and 8 we have discussed the 20 powers granted to the federal government by the states; also the things Congress is forbidden to do, the things the states are forbidden to do, and the things the states cannot do unless Congress consents.

Lesson 9 examines the most powerful political office in the world—the Presidency of the United States.

9

The Most Powerful Political Office in the World—The Presidency of the United States

Introduction

It would be interesting to know how the Founding Fathers would have reacted if someone had disclosed to them that within 200 years the President and executive branch of the United States government would become the power center of the world.

President Ronald Reagan

The original intent of the Founding Fathers to limit the powers of the federal government was carefully spelled out in their writings.

I

A. James Madison pointed out that the Constitution was structured so that "the powers delegated...to the federal government are few." He also pointed out that "the number of individuals employed under the Constitution of the United States will be much _smaller_ than the number employed under the particular States." (*Federalist Papers*, No. 45.)

B. In Washington's day there were 350 civilian employees serving a population of 3 million. Today (1985) there are approximately 231 million or 77 times more people, so the government would have to have at least 27,000 civilian employees to maintain services at the 1790s level. But suppose that modern

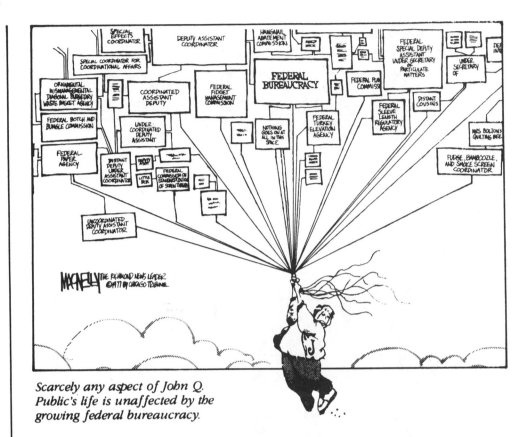

Scarcely any aspect of John Q. Public's life is unaffected by the growing federal bureaucracy.

complex circumstances require 10 times more government workers than Washington had. That would mean 270,000 workers today.

Since we have approximately *3 million* government employees, that makes the ratio of government workers compared to the number of people they serve ___*100*___ times greater in our day than in Washington's era.

C. The Founders contemplated heavy responsibilities for the President but limited them to six areas. Here are those six areas of presidential responsibility as they apply to our own day. The President is:

1. Chief of state over 231 million Americans.

2. Commander in chief over a military force of 3 million.

3. The chief executive officer of the whole executive branch of the government.

4. The chief diplomat in handling foreign relations.

5. The chief architect for needed legislation.

6. The conscience of the nation in granting pardons or reprieves where he feels justice requires them.

D. The Founders would be amazed to learn that under the influence of a European centralist philosophy known as democratic socialism (government control of the economy with the consent of the people's representatives), the President has been burdened with a host of other responsibilities never dreamed of by the Founders. Here are some of the things Congress has assigned the President:

1. The responsibility of maintaining _full_ employment for the work force of the entire nation.
2. The task of ensuring a high level of _agricultural_ prosperity.
3. The task of developing a national _housing_ program.
4. The task of supervising the exclusive distribution of _atomic_ energy resources.
5. Settling national _labor_-management disputes.
6. Providing various kinds of federal _relief_ for the victims of natural disasters throughout the country.
7. Administering a national _welfare_ program.
8. Administering a national _Medicare_ and Medicaid program.
9. Administering a national _social security_ program which is virtually bankrupting the government.
10. Allocating billions of dollars for _educating_ the young.
11. Administering a network of public _health_ agencies.
12. Administering the _environmental_ protection of the entire nation.
13. Administering nearly _40_ percent of the nation's land and its resources.
14. Administering supervisory control over the discovery and development of all major _energy_ resources.
15. _Regulating_ all major U.S. industries such as steel, automobile manufacturing, coal mining, oil production, metal mining, etc.
16. Supervising and licensing all _radio_ and _television_ broadcasting in the United States.
17. Monitoring the manufacturing and distribution of _food_ and _drug_ and requiring special permission before any drugs can be distributed.
18. Initiating various types of federal programs on a _regional_ basis to replace many powers and activities originally reserved to the sovereign states.

E. Not one of the above additions to the President's powers and responsibilities has been authorized by a constitutional _Amendment_. The states should have been consulted. Constitutional authorities doubt that any of these acts of Congress would have been ratified by three-fourths of the states if they had been presented to the states as amendments.

F. Furthermore, they are all outside the original intent of the Founders as set forth by Madison when he said:

The powers delegated by the proposed Constitution to the federal government are few and defined.... The powers reserved to the several States will extend to all the objects which, in the ordinary course of affairs, concern the lives, liberties, and properties of the people, and the internal order, improvement, and prosperity of the ___state___." (Ibid.)

G. What disadvantages did the Founders anticipate would result from the assigning of these responsibilities to the federal level?

1. It would be too ___expensive___. Private or local handling is cheaper.

2. Experience has indicated that government machinery operates at a low level of ___efficiency___.

3. It places billions of dollars at the disposal of the executive branch that can be (and have been) used to intimidate ___Congress___ and the ~~the~~ ___states___

4. It is humanly impossible for one person to administer this many responsibilities.

II

How the Founders structured the office of President as the chief servant of the people.

A. Article II, Section 1: The office of President.

In setting up this office, the Founders were pioneering. They had to answer numerous questions, including:

1. How many Presidents should there be?

   a. James Wilson recommended ___1___.

   b. Governor Randolph of Virginia recommended ___3___.

   c. The New Jersey Plan recommended ___several___.

2. What qualifications should be required of a candidate for President? It is interesting that they did *not* include:

   a. Any particular ___educational___ background.

   b. Or any ___property___ holdings.

3. Who should elect the President? This question required ___60___ ballots before the Convention decided on the electoral college.

4. Is the executive power of the United States vested in the President or in the executive branch of the federal government? It is all vested in the ___president___.

   a. Would it, therefore, be illegal for an administrative agency to conduct itself contrary to the instructions of the President? ___Yes___, if the President's instructions were within the ___law___.

b. Therefore, should he be able to discharge those who defy his instructions? ___yes___.

c. Why is this seldom done? Because of the protection of government employees under ___Civil___ ___Service___ regulations.

d. About how many are discharged each year? About ___1___ out of every 10,000 employees.

e. Has this seriously impeded the work of the Executive Branch? ___yes___.

5. What is the President's term of office? ___4___ years.

a. Would it be better to limit the President to a single term of six years? ___No___.

b. Why can the President only serve two terms? The Twenty-second Amendment was passed after the death of Franklin D. Roosevelt, who served 12 years and had just started his fourth term when he died.

6. The Founders considered four different ways to choose the President. What were they?

a. By the ___House___ and ___Senate___.

b. By the ___Governor___ of the states.

c. By ___popular___ vote of the people.

d. By appointing ___electors___ from each of the states.

7. In the original Electoral College, how many candidates did each elector vote for? ___two___.

a. What changed this? The ___Twelfth___ Amendment.

b. Did the Founders anticipate a two-party system? ___No___.

c. Has this worked out better than a multiparty system such as most other countries have? ___Yes___.

d. How many electors can each state have? The same number as the total of that state's ___Senators___ and ___Representatives___.

e. In a close election, is it possible for the popular election to go one way and the vote in the Electoral College to go the other? ___Yes___.

f. Is each elector required to vote the choice of his party? ___No___, but they nearly always do.

g. Can a government employee serve as an elector? ___No___.

h. When do the electors meet to give their vote? The second ___Monday___ in ___December___ following their election.

i. Where do they meet? Usually at the ___Capitol___ of their respective states.

8. Who can serve as President? He must be:

   a. A __natural__-born citizen or a citizen at the time of the adoption of the Constitution in 1789.

   b. He must have attained the age of __35__.

   c. He must have been a resident of the United States for at least __14__ years.

9. What happens if the President dies or is impeached or is unable to function in his office? This was finally worked out in the __25TH__ Amendment, which has some dangerous weaknesses that we will discuss in lesson 12. For example, this amendment does not provide for a line of succession in case several top officers are killed or become unavailable for service.

10. How much is the President paid each year? __400,000__. In addition:

    a. How much does he receive for annual expenses connected with his official duties? __50,000__.

    b. What does he receive after retirement? __60,000__ per year plus free mailing privileges, free office space, and $90,000 for office help. If he dies, his wife gets a pension of $20,000 per year.

    c. What was the salary of the first President of the United States? __25,000__—but George Washington declined to receive any compensation during his eight years as President.

11. Before taking office, a President is required to take an oath in which he pledges two things. What are they?

    a. To faithfully __execute__ the duties of President.

    b. To preserve, protect, and defend the __Constitution__.

    When was the phrase "So help me God" added to the oath? George Washington used it on his own initiative, but it did not become an official part of the oath until __1862__, when it was incorporated into the oath by an act of Congress.

Inauguration of Washington.

B. Article II, Section 2.

1. The President is the commander in chief of the armed services of the United States. He is also the commander of the militia of the several states when they are called into active duty. Could the Congress put someone else in charge of the military? __No__.

2. Is there a specific provision in the Constitution for the President's Cabinet? __No__, but it refers to the "principal officer" of each executive department from whom the President can require an opinion or a report in writing.

3. The President has the power to grant "reprieves and pardons."

   a. What is a reprieve? It is the power to __postpone__ the execution of a sentence, particularly a death sentence, until a certain time has passed or certain conditions are satisfied.

   b. What is a pardon? It is the power to excuse a person from being __punished__ for a crime or series of crimes.

      (1) Must a person be formally convicted of a crime before he can be pardoned? __No__. The Constitution says that the President can pardon an individual for an "__offense__" whether he has been formally convicted or not.

      (2) Can a person be pardoned after he has been impeached? __No__, because the power to impeach is granted to Congress as a check against the officers of the executive branch.

4. When the President makes a treaty with a foreign power, what is necessary before the treaty can go into effect? It must have the approval of __2/3__ of the Senators present at one of its session.

   a. How has the President circumvented this at summit conferences? By making what are known as "__executive__ agreements" with the heads of foreign countries.

   b. What is the remedy? An __Act__ of __Congress__ is all that would be necessary.

5. The President is empowered to nominate ambassadors, judges, and other important officers of the government. Congress may designate which positions are to require the "advice and consent" of the Senate.

   a. Does it require a two-thirds vote in the Senate to approve an appointment, or merely a majority of those present? __Majority__.

   b. What about the appointment of "inferior officers" in the executive and judicial branches? Congress can authorize these to be appointed by the __heads__ of departments.

   c. What if an important position requiring the "advice and consent" of the Senate becomes vacant while Congress is not in session? The President may __commission__ someone to fill that job, but his commission will expire if the Senate has not approved him by the end of the next session.

C. Article II, Section 3.

1. How often may the President address Congress on the state of the Union? As often as he feels it is __Necessary__. Must he deliver it in person? __No__.

2. Can the President recommend to Congress certain legislation which he feels is necessary? __Yes__.

a. Is there any authority for the President or the White House to lobby for such legislation? __No__.

b. What is the most powerful legislative lobby in Washington today? The __White__ __House__.

3. If Congress has adjourned, may the President call it back into session? __Yes__, for "extraordinary" occasions such as the threat of war or a financial emergency.

4. In case the House and the Senate cannot agree on a time of adjournment, may the President designate a specific time when it must take place? __Yes__, but this has never been necessary.

5. The President is to receive ambassadors and public ministers from foreign nations.

a. Who usually handles this function? The __State__ Department.

b. What if an ambassador becomes objectionable after he has been formally received? He is given his passport and is required to depart immediately.

6. The President is required to see that the laws of the United States are "faithfully executed." What if he considers a law unconstitutional or is opposed to it on principle? First of all, he can exercise his __veto__ power over any bill that comes to him for signature; but if Congress passes it over his veto, then he must "faithfully execute" it. Nevertheless, Presidents and Cabinet officers do have some prerogatives available to thwart what they consider to be bad laws. While Ezra Taft Benson was serving as Secretary of Agriculture, he persuaded the vast majority of farmers that it was to their disadvantage to sign agriculture assistance contracts. He was also successful in getting the cattlemen and dairy industries to resist the lure of various government subsidies. When he left office, __80__ percent of all American agriculture had been liberated from government controls. Since then, much of it has drifted back again.

*Former
Secretary of
Agriculture
Ezra Taft Benson*

D. Article II, Section 4.

1. By what means can the President, Vice President, or any other civil officers of the government be removed from office? By *impeachment* proceedings initiated by the House and tried in the Senate.

2. What are the offenses for which impeachment charges can be brought against an officer of the government?

   a. _Treason_.
   b. _Bribery_.
   c. _high crimes_ and _misdemeanors_

3. Has any president ever been impeached? _yes_ (2 – Johnson/Clinton) but not convicted.

   a. Who missed it by merely one vote? _Andrew Johnson_.

   b. Who is the only President who ever resigned under the threat of impeachment? _Richard Nixon_.

President Andrew Johnson

The White House
Washington

August 9, 1974

Dear Mr. Secretary:

I hereby resign the Office of President of the United States.

        Sincerely,

        /s/ Richard Nixon

The Honorable Henry A. Kissinger
The Secretary of State
Washington, D.C. 20520

Eleven words that made history.

Conclusion

The executive branch of the United States government has now become the power center of the world. Power blocs representing labor, business, multinational bankers, tax-exempt foundations, multinational corporations, promoters of the United Nations, and the advocates of a global or one-world government have all tried to capture this branch of the American government.

The unconstitutional expansion of the power of the President includes the following:

1. Making new laws by issuing executive orders published in the *Federal Register.*

2. Imposing highly restrictive or regulatory laws on the domestic affairs of the American people through the administration of federal agencies.

3. Entering into executive agreements with foreign nations (sometimes in complete secrecy) so as to evade the necessity of making formal treaties that would have to be approved by the Senate.

4. Administering the distribution of tens of billions of dollars in government projects, which gives the President tremendous power to influence the votes of Senators and Congressmen whose districts and states might be the recipeints of this money.

5. Administering billions of dollars in foreign aid (appropriated by Congress), which can be given or withheld according to the President's sympathy or hostility toward the economic and political philosophy of a particular country.

6. Making grants of federal funds dependent on the willingness of the recipient to accept the policies and guidelines imposed unilaterally by federal administrators in Washington or their regional offices.

10

The U.S. Supreme Court—Guardian of the Constitution

Introduction

Under the Articles of Confederation the Founders hoped all disputes could be solved in the state courts. Therefore, no federal system of courts was provided. It soon became apparent, however, that a higher court system was essential.

Article III—Structure of the Federal Judicial System

The Founders assigned to the federal system of courts eleven different types of disputes:

I

A. Cases involving the meaning or application of the ___Constitution___.

B. Cases arising under the ___laws___ passed by Congress.

C. Cases involving disputes between the United States and foreign powers.

D. Cases affecting ambassadors or other officials of foreign governments.

E. Cases relating to the admiralty or maritime problems.

F. Cases in which the United States is a party.

G. Disputes between two or more ___states___.

H. Disputes in which the citizen of one state sues another state. (Repealed by the ___11th___ Amendment following the case of *Chisholm* v. *Georgia* in 1793.)

I. Disputes between citizens of different states (Congress later added the proviso that such cases had to be of some importance, involving $___10,000___ or more).

J. Disputes between citizens of the same state over claims or land grants in different states.

K. Cases involving suits between a state or citizen of a state and a foreign government or citizen of a foreign government.

II When the federal court system was finally set up by Congress, it had **three** levels:

A. The ___district___ court, where federal cases are initiated. Originally there was one to each state, but today there are 144 federal district courts.

B. The circuit courts of ___appeal___. There are now nine circuit courts.

C. The ___Supreme___ Court, the court of final appeal.

The Supreme Court Building, Washington, D.C.

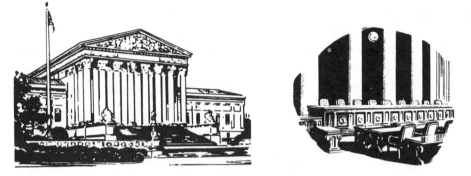

1. There are two types of cases which both begin and end in the Supreme Court (Section 2, Clause 2):
   a. Those cases involving high officials of ___foreign___ countries such as ambassadors and consuls.
   b. Where one of the ___States___ is a party to the suit and the matter involves federal jurisdiction.

2. The Supreme Court will not review or hold hearings on all cases referred to it, but only those where the court is not satisfied with the ruling of the lower courts. Out of 5,000 appeals each year, the Supreme Court only accepts around ___200___ for further analysis or hearings.

D. Congress is authorized to set up additional courts as needed. These are called ___special___ courts and usually involve technical issues such as taxes, customs, patents, and claims against the United States government.

III Section 2, Clause 3 provides that in all federal criminal cases, the trial shall be by ___jury___. (The Seventh Amendment also provides for a jury in civil suits where the amount is in excess of ___20___ dollars.)

It is interesting that the jury referred to here was the common law jury, which could pass on the law as well as "find" the facts. In 1895 the Supreme Court excluded the jury from determining the law, and thereby greatly weakened one of the safety nets the Founders had provided to protect the rights of the people.

A. It should be observed that the Founders did not give the federal government any general ___police___ power, but only authority to investigate and prosecute such matters as:

1. Crimes on Indian reservations.

2. Counterfeiting.

3. Robbery of federally insured banks.

4. Interstate crimes such as interstate transportation of stolen automobiles and other goods, white slavery and kidnapping, etc.

5. Crimes related to national ___security___, such as espionage and sabotage.

B. The states were extremely anxious to prohibit the development of a national police system.

1. J. Edgar Hoover flatly ___refused___ to head up a national police service during the gangster era. He said it would mark the end of America's democratic republic.

2. Federal agents were not authorized by Congress to carry weapons until a number were ___killed___ while conducting investigations.

3. Civil rights violations can only be investigated and prosecuted by the federal government. They cannot be prevented by federal "policing." That is a primary responsibility of each state.

J. Edgar Hoover

The Founders also made the federal courts the guardian of the Constitution.

A. They set up a strictly ___limited___ government of carefully defined powers because, as Washington said:

> Government is not reason, it is not eloquence—it is ___force___! Like fire, it is a dangerous servant and a fearful master. (Jacob M. Braude, *Life-Time Speaker's Encyclopedia*, 2 vols., Englewood Cliffs, N.J.: Prentice-Hall, 1962, 1:326.)

B. The federal courts were to keep both the states and the officers of the federal government within the boundaries of the Constitution. (See *Federalist Papers,* No. 78.)

C. They were to interpret the Constitution very ___strictly___ as the Founders originally designed it. The courts have no authority to interpret it any other way. (Ibid.)

1. Chief Justice Taney expressed the traditional view of the law when he wrote in the *Dred Scott* decision:

> It [the Constitution] speaks not only in the same words, but with the same meaning and intent with which it spoke when it came from then hands of the framers. (19 Howard 395; 60 U.S. 393.)

IV

2. Justice Thomas Cooley wrote:

> The meaning of the Constitution is fixed when adopted, and it is not different at any subsequent time. The object of construction, as applied to a written Constitution, is to give effect to the intent of the people in adopting it. (*Constitutional Limitations*, pp. 68–69.)

D. By 1821, it was apparent to Jefferson that the Constitution had not provided an adequate check on the Supreme Court. He felt it was already beginning to deprive the people and the states of their constitutional rights as it concentrated more and more power in Washington, D.C. He wrote:

> It has long, however, been my opinion . . . that the germ of dissolution of our federal government is in the constitution of the federal judiciary . . . working like gravity by night and by day, gaining a little today and little tomorrow, and advancing its noiseless step like a thief, over the field of jurisdiction, until all shall be usurped from the States, and the government of all be consolidated into one. To this I am opposed; because when all government . . . shall be drawn to Washington as the centre of all power, it will render powerless the checks provided . . . and will become as venal and oppressive as the government [of George III] from which we separated. (Albert Ellery Bergh, ed., *The Writings of Thomas Jefferson*, 20 vols., Washington: Thomas Jefferson Memorial Foundation, 1907, 15:330–32.)

E. What is the remedy for this unauthorized power play by the Supreme Court?

1. A Constitution-oriented _Congress_ is required—one that is willing to come to grips with the unconstitutional usurpation of power by the federal courts.

2. Congress or a convention of the states could initiate a judicial reform amendment to protect the people and the _states_ from this type of unconstitutional activity. This amendment would probably need to do at least two things:

   a. Allow a decision of the court to be overturned by a _2/3_ vote of the House and Senate or _3/4_ of the state legislatures.

   b. Require Supreme Court Justices to have five years of judicial experience, with three of those years having been spent as a justice of a state supreme court or as a judge of a federal court. Perhaps the Justices of the Supreme Court should also be prohibited from serving beyond age 75 or for more than 15 years.

V The purpose and design of the United States Constitution was to define the structure of our government and the relationship between its various parts. Specific legislation and definitions of crimes were therefore not included except in one instance. That exception was the crime of _treason_.

A. In England, the king and Parliament had used the offense of treason as an excuse to:

    1. Hang the leaders of ___political___ opposition groups (such as Sir Walter Raleigh in the days of James I).

    2. Confiscate their rich ___family___ estates.

B. England had a total of ___17___ different offenses that were classified as "treason" during the colonial period.

C. Article III, Section 2 reduced the crime of treason to only two offenses:

    1. To engage in (the waging) or levying of ___WAR___ against the United States.

    2. To adhere to an enemy of the United States by giving that enemy ___aid___ and ___comfort___.

Sir Walter Raleigh

D. The Supreme Court has held that a foreign power does not constitute an "enemy" within the meaning of this provision until Congress has actually declared ___war___ against that nation.

but that does not restrict enemy to nations.

    1. In two of our worst wars, Congress did not actually declare war because they were supposed to be merely ___police___ actions under United Nations regional treaties. These were:

        a. The three-year war in ___Korea___.

        b. The ten-year war in ___Vietnam___.

    2. In both of these wars, prominent Americans who were sympathetic with the Communist philosophy actually put on drives for blood banks, money, and supplies to assist those who were fighting against the American forces. They could not be prosecuted for treason because there had been no formal declaration of war by Congress.

E. No person can be convicted of treason unless he confesses in open court or there are ___2___ or more witnesses to the same overt act.

Vietnam War

F. Congress is given the responsibility under Section 3 to declare the penalty for treason, and the U.S. Code states that the extreme penalty can be ___death___.

G. However, the Constitution specifically says that the punishment for treason cannot "work corruption of blood, or forfeiture [of property] except during the life" of the offender.

    1. This means that the punishment cannot be extended to penalize the offender's ___family___.

    2. As a result of this provision, large estates that had been confiscated and sold during the Civil War had to be returned to the heirs of the original owners after the latter had died. In other words, the punishment of a guilty person cannot extend to his family. The confiscated lands of the guilty person could only be sold for the duration of his lifetime.

Article IV—Relations Between the States

Prior to the adoption of the Constitution in 1789, many of the states were treating other states as foreign powers. Article IV was designed to solve some of the most abrasive problems that had arisen among the thirteen original states. The Founders also wanted to cover additional problems that might arise as new states came into the Union.

I

Article IV, Section 1: Should the acts of one state be binding on all the rest of the states?

A. Section 1 provides that the official acts of each state must receive full ___faith___ and ___credit___ by all the other states.

B. It also provided that Congress is to decide what ___proof___ would be required to show what the official acts of a state might have been.

II

Article IV, Section 2: "The citizens of each state shall be entitled to all privileges and immunities of citizens in the several states."

A. "Privileges and immunities" refers to the ___natural___ rights of citizens to travel freely, set up businesses, sue in the courts, have the protection of property, etc.

B. It does not include ___acquired___ rights of citizens in each of the states. These are advantages that the people of a particular state have developed at great expense to the taxpayers of that state.

   1. This would include such things as ___hunting___, fishing, attending state-supported colleges, trucking over its roads, etc.

   2. In these cases, extra ___fees___ can be charged to citizens of other states.

III

Article IV, Section 2: What happens when a criminal flees from one state to another in order to escape detection or punishment for his crime?

A. The governor of the state where the crime was committed can demand the ___return___ of the fugitive for prosecution or punishment. This is called a request for "extradition' of the alleged offender.

B. Is the return of the offender mandatory? The Supreme Court has held that it is discretionary with the governor of the state where the alleged offender is residing. He is allowed to determine whether he believes it is ___safe___ or just to have the offender extradited to another state.

IV

Article IV, Section 2: When any person is under an obligation of "service" (slaves and bond servants) and that person enters a state where such relationships are illegal, the slave or bond servant is not automatically discharged from his obligations but must be delivered up on demand to the person to whom such service is due. This entire provision is now _obsolete_ as a result of the Thirteenth Amendment.

Article IV, Section 3: The creation of new states.   **V**

A. New states can be created by:

   1. _Dividing_ existing states.

   2. _Combining_ existing states.

   3. _Creating_ new states out of federal territories.

B. However, this can only be done with the consent of Congress and the legislatures of any states involved.

C. The Northwest Ordinance adopted by Congress on July 13, 1787, provided that all new states would enter the Union "on an _equal_ footing with the original states in all respects whatever." (Article V.)

   1. The states created east of the Mississippi and those from the Louisiana Purchase all came in on an _equal_ basis.

   2. However, in the western states and Alaska, the federal government has permanently retained vast quantities of their lands. Efforts are now being made to rectify this injustice. The press has called it the "_Sagebrush_ Rebellion," but it is not a rebellion. The western states are simply using established constitutional procedures to recover the land unlawfully withheld from them.

Article IV, Section 3: Only _Congress_ shall have the power to regulate or dispose of territory or property belonging to the United States.   **VI**

This provision was completely ignored in the giving away of the Panama Canal.

A. Instead of going to Congress as required by the Constitution, the President _Carter_ signed it away by means of a _treaty_.

B. The Senate was then induced to _ratify_ the treaty, but the House of Representatives was never consulted. The House made strong demands on the Senate to be a party to the transaction, but its constitutional rights were denied.

Article IV, Section 3: The United States shall guarantee a _republican_ or representative form of government in each of the states.   **VII**

A. The use of the _initiative_ referendum by many of the states is a technical violation of this provision but has not been seriously challenged.

B. Under this provision, the federal government has the responsibility to protect each of the states from _invasion_ by another state or a foreign power.

C. The federal government is also given the responsibility of responding to the request of a state legislature or its governor (if the legislature is not in session) to help suppress an insurrection or domestic ___violence___ such as rioting.

Article V—The Amending Process

The Founders learned that they had made a mistake when they specified that the Articles of Confederation could only be amended with the consent of ___all___ the states. Several times a single, obstinate state prevented that document from being strengthened with needed amendments.

The provisions of Article V were, therefore, considered extremely important by the Founders.

I

There are two ways the Constitution can be amended, but only the first one has ever been used.

A. The first method is by having the amendment approved by:

1. ___2/3, 2/3___ of the House and the Senate.

2. And <u>then</u> approved by ___3/4___ of the state legislatures or state conventions.

B. The second method is to have ___2/3___ of the state legislatures petition Congress for a constitutional convention. Ratification then involves three steps:

1. Congress calls upon the states to send delegates to a constitutional convention, indicating the place and date.

2. The convention of <u>delegates</u> from the various states can then prepare and vote on the proposed amendment.

3. Any proposed amendments must then be approved by ___3/4___ of the state legislatures. (Notice that the approval of Congress and the President is not required under this method.)

II

There are two restrictions to the amending process:

A. No amendment giving the federal government control over the slave trade was to be passed before ___1808___. This was to give the South the opportunity to phase out slavery during the next twenty years so that its economy would not be disrupted.

B. It was also provided that no state, without its ___consent___, can be deprived of equal representation in the Senate. The recent amendment proposed by Congress to give the District of Columbia two Senators and a Congressman was a definite violation of this provision. This is one of the main reasons why so many states refused to ratify it.

Article VI—Federal Supremacy

The setting up of a national government of the people imposed certain obligations on the federal government in conjunction with its newly acquired powers. There were three areas that needed to be spelled out very specifically, and this article attempted to cover them.

Article VI, Section 1: "All _debts_ contracted and engagements entered into, before the adoption of this Constitution, shall be as valid against the United States . . . as under the Confederation."

A. Under the Confederation, the states had accrued debts amounting to approximately _25 million_ as a result of the Revolutionary War.

B. The additional debts of the federal government accrued since the Declaration of Independence brought the total indebtedness of the United States to around _73 million_. A major part of this debt was owed to foreign countries.

C. This provision announced to the world that the new government would be economically responsible and _honor_ its legitimate obligations of the past.

I

Article VI, Section 2: The supremacy of federal law over that of the states.

A. There are three areas of federal law to which the laws and actions of the states are subordinate:

1. The _Constitution_.

2. _laws_ established by the federal government.

3. _treaties_ entered into by the United States.

B. Note that there is no reference here to executive agreements by the President with foreign powers; no reference to executive orders; no reference to edicts by regulatory agencies; and no reference to edicts by the Supreme Court, which constitute judicial legislation. The question turns on what the Founders meant by "laws of the United States . . . made in pursuance" of the provisions set forth in the Constitution.

C. The judges of the state are bound by the provisions of the Constitution, federal law, and federal treaties, "any thing in the _Constitution_ or laws of any state to the contrary notwithstanding."

II

Article VI, Section 3: To ensure complete loyalty to the Union, all Senators, Representatives, officials, and judges of the United States as well as officials of the individual states were required to take an _oath_ or affirmation that they would uphold the U.S. Constitution. However, no religious test was to be required in connection with the oath.

III

oathkeepers.org

Article VII—Ratification

It should be kept in mind that the Constitution was written under circumstances that were threatening to dissolve the Union. There was a serious question as to whether every state would ratify the Constitution with sufficient promptness to get the new government into operation soon enough to solve the problems plaguing the nation.

I

This article provides that: "The ratification of the conventions of __9__ states, shall be sufficient for the establishment of this Constitution between the states so ratifying the same."

   A. This new Constitution was only to be binding upon the states that actually ratified it.

   B. There was no provision to __compel__ dissident states to come in under the new Constitution, even though they had previously entered into a "confederation and perpetual union."

Ratification of the Constitution: The numbers indicate the order in which the states ratified.

Conclusion

This is the form in which the Constitution was finally submitted to Congress and the states in September 1787. The Constitution was adopted by 11 of the states by 1788, and after elections were held in these states, the new Constitution was considered to be in full force and effect as of March 4, 1789. However, President Washington was not inaugurated until April 30, and after that both North Carolina and Rhode Island joined the Union.

To get the states to ratify the Constitution, it was necessary to open the Constitution to further amendments suggested by the states. They submitted 189, and these were finally consolidated into the 10 provisions now known as the Bill of Rights.

In our next lesson we will discuss "America's Famous Bill of Rights."

a bit of a misnomer because in English law a "Bill of Rights" defined only what rights there were.

11

America's Famous Bill of Rights

Introduction

The American Bill of Rights is a legacy from tens of thousands of Englishmen who suffered torture, hanging, beheading, imprisonment, exile, and being burned alive in an effort to preserve those basic rights of freemen set forth in:

1. The Magna Charta of 1215.
2. The Petition of Rights of 1628.
3. The Writ of Habeas Corpus in 1679.
4. The English Bill of Rights of 1689.

The Founders wrote a preamble to the Bill of Rights which is seldom included in printed texts of the Constitution anymore:

"The Conventions of a number of states, having at the time of their adopting the Constitution, expressed a desire, in order to prevent misconstruction or abuse of its [the federal government's] powers, that further declaratory and restrictive clauses be added...."

The First Amendment

A. The First Amendment begins with these words: "Congress shall make ___no___ law respecting an ___establishment___ of religion, or prohibiting the free exercise thereof."

I

1. The Founders had already declared in the Northwest Ordinance of 1787 that "religion" should be taught in the ___schools___. But they did not want the government backing any particular "establishment" of religion—that is, the creed and ritual of a particular church.

2. They used the term "religion" in its broadest sense, meaning the basic beliefs in which practically all mankind agree. According to Franklin and others of the Founders, these basic beliefs are:

   a. The "self-evident" truth that there is a ___Creator___ who made all things.

   b. That the Creator has revealed a ___moral___ code which defines what is right and what is wrong.

   c. That the Creator holds mankind responsible for the way they ___treat___ each other.

   d. That all mankind ___live___ beyond this life.

Bill of Rights

Congress of the United States

begun and held at the City of New-York, on
Wednesday the fourth of March, one thousand seven hundred and eighty nine

---

e. That in the next life individuals are ___judged___ by the Creator for their conduct in this one.

3. The Founders held these universal religious beliefs to be an extremely important part of the American system of ___government___ as well as our culture. As we have previously mentioned:

a. Samuel Adams said that these basic beliefs which constitute "the religion of America [are] the religion of all ___mankind___." (William V. Wells, *The Life and Public Service of Samuel Adams*, 3 vols., Boston: Little, Brown and Company, 1865, 3:23.)

or "– an organized system of beliefs that caused people to be good –"

    b. John Adams called these tenets the "general __*principle*__ "
on which the American civilization was founded. (Albert Ellery Bergh,
ed., *The Writings of Thomas Jefferson,* 20 vols., Washington: Thomas
Jefferson Memorial Association, 1907, 13:293.)

    c. Thomas Jefferson called these basic beliefs the principles "in which
God has __*united*__ us all." (Ibid., 14:198.)

    d. In his Farewell Address (1796), Washington spoke of these religious
principles as the "indispensable __*supports*__ " of good
government. He said that there is no "security for property, for
reputation, for life, if the sense of religious obligation" is lost from
among the people. Their oaths in court and their oaths in assuming
high office would become meaningless.

4. The Founders said that these fundamental beliefs were important
because human beings tend to behave the way they __*believe*__.
Therefore, the tremendous influence of these beliefs on the American
culture was immediately apparent to Alexis de Tocqueville when he
visited the United States in 1831. He wrote:

> On my arrival in the United States the religious aspect of the country
> was the first thing that struck my attention; and the longer I stayed
> there, the more I perceived the great political consequences
> resulting from this __*new*__ state of things.

He described the situation as follows:

> Religion in America takes no direct part in the government of
> society, but it must be regarded as the __*first*__ of their political
> institutions;...I am certain that they hold it to be indispensable to
> the maintenance of __*Republican*__ institutions [a
> government of the people by elected representatives]. This opinion
> is not peculiar to a class of citizens or to a party, but it belongs to the
> whole nation and to every rank of society. (*Democracy in America*,
> 12th ed., 2 vols., New York: Vintage Books, 1945, 1:319, 316.)

Alexis de Tocqueville

B. The second provision of the First Amendment is that "Congress shall make
__*no*__ law...abridging the freedom of speech, or of the press."

1. The Founders knew there would have to be some reasonable restrictions
on this freedom, but they wanted such regulations and standards of
propriety to be handled on the state level, close to the people, in order to
eliminate __*abuse*__ when they occur.

2. The states have restricted freedom of speech and the press to:

    a. Prevent false attacks on individuals in the form of libel or
__*slander*__.

    b. Prevent speech which endangers life, such as falsely shouting "Fire!"
in a crowded theater.

    c. Prevent individuals from inciting riots or promoting insurrection by

advocating the overthrow of government by ___force___ and violence. Amazingly, in *Yates* vs *U.S.* (354 U.S. 298) the Supreme Court nullified state statutes containing this provision.

C. The third provision of the First Amendment is that "Congress shall make ___no___ law...abridging...the right of the people peaceably to ___assemble___."

D. The First Amendment also provides that "Congress shall make ___no___ law...abridging...the right of the people...to ___petition___ the government for a redress of grievances."

II *The Second Amendment*

The Second Amendment reads: "A well-regulated militia being necessary to the security of a free state, the right of the people to keep and bear arms shall not be infringed."

A. The militia of a state is that body of citizens which, under law, can be called up by the ___governor___ or Congress to protect the rights and security of the people.

1. Many Americans do not even know that they belong to the militia of their state. They confuse their state militia with the National Guard, which is a specialized reserve corps in each state trained at federal expense for immediate service.

2. Under the U.S. Code, Title 10, section 31, the militia of each state includes "all able-bodied ___males___ at least ___17___ years of age and under ___45___ years of age who are or have [made] a declaration of intent to become citizens."

3. If the Equal Rights Amendment had been adopted, this provision would also include all ___females___ between those ages.

B. The right to bear arms was considered by the Founders to be an ___inalienable___ right connected with the preservation of life, liberty, and property. Notice that any regulation of firearms was left exclusively under the control of the states.

1. Today, Americans are the best-armed civilian population in the world.

   a. The number of private citizens owning arms is estimated to be around ___50___ million.

   b. The number of firearms in the possession of private citizens is estimated to be between ___150___ and ___200___ million.

2. In nations where the leaders want to suppress the people by depriving them of their property and freedom, they begin by trying to disarm them.

   a. First they merely ask them to ___register___ their guns and impose a heavy penalty on any who do not.

   b. Then they sometimes deliberately provoke rioting and violence and use this as an excuse to _confiscate_ all arms in the possession of private citizens.

The Third Amendment

III

The Third Amendment is as follows: "No soldier shall, in time of peace, be quartered in any house without the consent of the owner, nor in time of war, but in a manner to be prescribed by law."

A. European kings used the practice of quartering troops in the homes of the people to _save_ money or to quell a rebellion. In either case, there was often an extensive destruction of property and _abuse_ of the women and girls in the home.

B. In 1765, King George III tried to quarter troops in the colonies to enforce the Stamp Act.

    1. According to the king's orders, troops were to be quartered in the people's homes and provided with "fire, candles, vinegar and salt, bedding, utensils for dressing their victuals...without _paying_ anything for the same."

    2. The citizens of Massachusetts flatly _refused_ to obey the order.

King George III's infamous Quartering Act infuriated the colonists in Massachusetts.

The Fourth Amendment

The Fourth Amendment was designed to protect the privacy of the people in their homes and their possessions:

"The right of the people to be secure in their persons, houses, papers, and effects, against unreasonable searches and seizures, shall not be violated, and no warrants shall issue but upon probable cause, supported by oath or affirmation, and particularly describing the place to be searched, and the persons or things to be seized."

A. Privacy is an essential element associated with the inalienable right to life, liberty, personal property, and the pursuit of ___happiness___. It is also an essential element of feeling ___secure___ in the enjoyment of the inalienable rights guaranteed under the Constitution.

B. Any search conducted by officers, whether by warrant or otherwise, must not be ___unreasonable___

  1. Would it be reasonable, in connection with an authorized arrest, to check the offender's car or immediate premises? ___Yes___.

  2. Would it be unreasonable for the police to chase a criminal across private property? ___No___.

  3. Would it be unreasonable for the police to enter on private property in order to make certain it was secure? ___No___.

  4. Would it be unreasonable to open mail, tap a telephone, or place electronic surveillance on an individual? ___Yes___, unless human ___life___ is in danger or the case involves a serious ___threat___ to the security of the nation.

C. Warrants are required to protect the basic rights of freedom and privacy.

  1. For an officer to obtain a warrant of arrest, he must be able to show the judge:

    a. Probable cause or reasonable ___evidence___ that the warrant is justified.

    b. That there is probable cause to believe that the person named in the warrant is responsible for the ___crime___.

    The officer must then take an oath or give an affirmation that what he has told the judge is ___true___.

  2. These strict provisions grew out of the colonists' experience with unjustified "writs of assistance" issued by the admiralty courts (in which there were no juries). Such writs allowed the officers to go on wild "fishing expeditions" in search of contraband.

V | *The Fifth Amendment*

The Fifth Amendment has five parts, each of which reiterates certain rights relating to life, liberty, and property:

A. A federal criminal charge must first be presented to a ___Grand___ jury.

B. No person can be tried twice for the same offense (placed in double jeopardy).

C. No person may be required to ___testify___ against himself.

D. No person may be deprived of life, liberty, or property, without ___due___ process of law.

The Bill of Rights guarantees the right to trial by jury.

E. No private property shall be taken for public use without ___just___ compensation.

↑ not benefit

The Sixth Amendment

VI

The Sixth Amendment states that once a person has been indicted for a federal crime, he has certain specific rights:

A. The accused is entitled to a speedy and ___public___ trial.

B. The accused has the right to be tried by an impartial ___jury___.

C. The jury must be selected from the ___state___ and ___district___ where the offense occurred.

D. The accused must be ___informed___ of the nature of the offense he is supposed to have committed.

E. The defendant is entitled to be confronted by his ___accusers___.

F. The defendant is entitled to have compulsory process for the obtaining of ___witness___ in his behalf.

G. An accused person is entitled to have the assistance of counsel for his ___defense___.

The Seventh Amendment

VII

The Seventh Amendment deals with common law or civil suits and has two parts:

A. "In suits at common law, where the value in controversy shall exceed ___20___ dollars, the right of trial by jury shall be preserved."

B. "No fact tried by a jury shall be otherwise reexamined in any court of the

United States than according to the rules of the common law."

1. This simply means that the judge cannot substitute his _opinion_ for the findings of fact by the jury.

2. However, the judge can:

    a. Order the jury to bring in a verdict in favor of the defendant where the facts presented do not constitute a _valid_ case against the defendant.

    b. Order a new trial where the verdict is clearly erroneous in view of the _facts_ and the requirements of the law.

VIII *The Eighth Amendment*

The Eighth Amendment has three parts:

A. The first part provides that excessive _bail_ shall not be required.

B. The second part provides that the defendant shall not have excessive _fines_ imposed.

C. The third part provides that the convicted person shall not be subjected to _cruel_ and unusual punishment.

IX *The Ninth Amendment*

The Ninth Amendment provides that: "The enumeration in the Constitution of certain rights shall not be construed to deny or disparage others retained by the people."

A. In the *Federalist Papers,* No. 84, Alexander Hamilton had argued that a Bill of Rights was _unnecessary_ because the law provided that a listing of things always assumed that it was all-inclusive and that any item left out was done so deliberately and, therefore, forfeited.

B. Under their theory of _limited_ government, the Founders wanted it understood that they were not forfeiting anything. Their constitutional rights included not only the ones they had mentioned but all other rights besides!

X *The Tenth Amendment*

The Tenth Amendment provides that: "The powers not delegated to the United States by the Constitution, nor prohibited by it to the states, are reserved to the states respectively, or to the people."

A. This amendment was designed to fix the " _chains_ of the Constitution" on the agencies and elected officals of the federal government. That is, unless the Constitution specifically spelled out an assigned duty to the federal government, it had *no* _authority_ to enter that field of endeavor.

Was President Theordore Roosevelt right when he said he was authorized to do anything unless the Constitution specifically prohibited him from doing it? _No_.

B. Constitutional authorities agree that today today this is the most widely _violated_ provision of the entire Constitution. The original intent of the Founders was repeated over and over in their writings. We have previously quoted Washington and Madison. Here is a statement from Thomas Jefferson:

> I believe the states can best govern our _internal_ concerns and the general government our _external_ ones. I wish, therefore, to see maintained that wholesome distribution of powers established by the Constitution for the limitation of both, and never to see all offices transferred to Washington. (Bergh, *The Writings of Thomas Jefferson*, 15:450–51.)

Conclusion

Thus we conclude our story of America's famous Bill of Rights, which has been copied in this or similar form in the constitutions of each of the states.

In our final lesson on the Constitution, we will cover the last sixteen amendments and tell the background of each.

12

The Last Seventeen Amendments

Introduction

Once Congress and the ratifying states adopted the Bill of Rights, it was assumed that little or nothing needed to be done to further perfect the nation's great charter of liberty.

However, in the next dozen years, two additional amendments were passed and ratified.

The Eleventh Amendment
(February 7, 1795)

XI

The Eleventh Amendment provided that a state could not be sued by the citizen of another state.

A. When a citizen from South Carolina named Chisholm sued the state of Georgia for a certain indebtedness, the federal court took jurisdiction and _Compelled_ Georgia to respond to the suit.

B. Therefore, the states felt that this amendment was necessary in order to protect the right of sovereignty of each of the states. This included the right of each state not to be sued without its _Consent_.

The Twelfth Amendment
(July 27, 1804)

XII

This amendment was designed to correct _weakness_ in the electoral college system, which is described in Article II, Section 1, Clause 3. It will be recalled that each elector was to vote for two candidates. The person getting the most votes became President, and the next in popularity became Vice President. The Twelfth Amendment provided that:

A. Each elector must submit _Separate_ ballots for President and Vice President.

B. A candidate for President must receive a _majority_ of the electoral votes to win.

   1. If three or more parties participate, the candidate with the most votes may still lack a _majority_.

   2. In that case, the names of not more than _3_ of those having the most votes are sent to the House of Representatives, where each state has one vote in selecting the winner.

C. A candidate for Vice President must also get a _~~very~~ majority_ of the electoral votes to win. In the absence of a majority for any one candidate, the names of the ___2___ highest are sent to the Senate, where a majority of the entire Senate determines the winner.

D. This amendment also provides that a person cannot qualify as a candidate for Vice President unless he has all of the qualifications required for ___President___. This was an oversight in the original Constitution.

XIII

The Thirteenth Amendment

(December 6, 1865) — *end of Civil War*

The Thirteenth Amendment has two sections:

A. "Neither slavery nor involuntary servitude, except as a punishment for crime...shall exist within the United States."

This amendment was adopted in 1865, two years _after_ President Lincoln's Emancipation Proclamation took effect. Why was this amendment necessary?

   1. President Lincoln's proclamation only covered those areas at ___war___ with the Union. It did not cover bond servants or slaves in other areas, including parts of Virginia and Louisiana and all of Tennessee.

   2. There was also some doubt as to whether the proclamation was within the ___~~clear~~ Constitution___ powers of the President. This amendment settled the constitutional question permanently.

B. "Congress shall have power to enforce this article by appropriate legislation." The only difficulty connected with its enforcement has been the proper interpretation of "involuntary servitude."

   1. Is there a violation if someone pays the fine for a prisoner and then forces him to work out the fine as an employee? ___Yes___.

   2. Is there a violation if a prisoner is required to work out his fine following conviction for a crime? ___No___.

   3. Is there a violation if a convicted prisoner is sentenced to a certain period at "hard labor"? ___No___.

   4. Is there a violation if a person signs a contract to work, say, in a movie and the court orders him to do it or pay damages? ___No___.

XIV

The Fourteenth Amendment

(July 9, 1868)

A. This amendment provides that all persons born or naturalized in the United States are automatically ___citizens___ with equal rights which cannot be abridged without due ___process___ of law.

B. Secondly, "No state shall make or enforce any law which shall abridge the privileges of immunities of citizens of the United States; nor shall any state deprive any person of life, liberty, or property, without due process of law;

nor deny to any person...the equal protection of the law."

It is this provision that has been used from 1925 (the *Gitlow* case) to the present to transfer a huge workload of cases to the federal courts.

C. This amendment also made all debts or claims against the Confederacy null and _Void_. This meant that all Confederate bonds and currency were declared worthless.

The Fifteenth Amendment

XV

(February 3, 1870)

The principal section of this amendment reads as follows:

"The right of citizens of the United States to vote shall not be denied or abridged by the United States or by any state on account of race, color, or previous condition of servitude."

A. Notice that the states were still allowed to determine qualifications for voters, but the rules must be the same for all citizens.

B. At the time of the adoption of this amendment (1869–70), all of the states still excluded _Women_ from voting. This was not remedied until the _Nineteenth_ Amendment was passed in 1920.

The Sixteenth Amendment

XVI

(February 3, 1913)

There are few, if any, amendments that have a more interesting _history_ than the famous Sixteenth Amendment, which authorized federal income taxes:

"The Congress shall have power to lay and collect taxes on incomes, from whatever source derived, without apportionment among the several states, and without regard to census or enumeration."

A. Income taxes are assessed directly against the individual and, therefore, constitute a _direct_ tax. Article I, Section 9, Clause 4, says that a direct tax must be apportioned to the states according to population, not according to individual income.

B. During the Civil War, Congress passed an income tax measure. The Supreme Court warped its legal vision sufficiently to call it an _indirect_ tax, so it was used during the emergency to help finance the war.

C. In 1894, the Supreme Court reversed itself and ruled that a federal income tax is a _direct_ tax after all and is therefore unconstitutional.

D. By 1905, the demands for redistribution of wealth through a federal income tax was growing in the liberal wings of both the Democrats and Republicans. The idea was to "soak the _rich_!"

E. In 1909, Senator Joseph W. Bailey, a Democrat from Texas, introduced an amendment to a tariff bill that would tax all incomes of $5,000 or more at

Taxes: The American people need help.

___2___ percent. This amendment was introduced to embarrass the Republicans by forcing them to openly oppose a measure that seemed to be gaining popularity.

F. When it appeared that the Bailey motion was actually going to pass, conservative Republicans frantically introduced an income tax bill as an _Amendment_ to the Constitution, confident that it would be rejected by enough states to defeat it. By this means, they felt, the Democrats would get from the states a clear idea of popular sentiments against income taxes.

G. The plan backfired. The Senate approved the income tax amendment ___77___ to ___0___ (after all, who wants to be against "soaking the rich"?), and the House approved it 318 to 14. And as one constitutional textbook reports: "Contrary to all expectations, the income tax amendment was ratified by one state legislature after another and was proclaimed in effect on February 25, _1913_." (Kelly and Harbison, *The American Constitution: Its Origins and Development,* 3d ed., New York: W. W. Norton and Co., 1963, pp. 625–26.)

H. Congressman S. E. Payne of New York, who had introduced the bill in the House for the Republicans, admitted that they were simply trying to defeat the Bailey bill and did not really want an income tax. He said that an income tax is "one that makes a nation of _liars_." (*Congressional Record,* 12 July 1909, p. 4404.)

I. Income tax rates have now risen ___10___ times higher than the original sponsors predicted.

The Seventeenth Amendment

(April 8, 1915)

XVII

It is important to know the historical background of this amendment, which mandates the election of Senators by popular vote:

A. George Washington was one of the foremost proponents of a Senate with members appointed by the state _legislatures_.

B. When Jefferson returned from France, he expressed concern as to the purpose of the Senate and why it was not elected by the people. Washington asked him why he poured his hot drink in his saucer before drinking it. Jefferson replied, "To _cool_ it." "And that," Washington commented, "is what the Senate is for." The Senate is to cool down any hotheaded or imprudent legislation from the House.

C. The purpose of the Senate was to veto any _radical_ movements designed to break down property rights, states' rights, and the established order of constitutional government. Senators were to represent the states as sovereign entities, and the Founders decided that the best way to achieve this would be by having the state legislatures appoint them.

D. The House responded to the demands of the populist movement and approved an amendment for the popular election of Senators in 1893, 1894, 1898, 1900, and 1902, but each time the Senate either _ignored_ it or voted it down.

E. The Seventeenth Amendment was finally pushed through both the House and the Senate in 1911 and was ratified by three-fourths of the states in _1913_.

F. Events since 1913 have demonstrated that the original _design_ of the Founders in setting up the Senate as a legislative guardian has been largely emasculated by the Seventeenth Amendment.

The Eighteenth Amendment

(January 16, 1919)

XVIII

The Eighteenth Amendment inaugurated the Prohibition era in the United States:

"After one year from the ratification of this article the manufacture, sale, or transportation of intoxicating liquors within, the importation thereof into, or the exportation thereof from the United States and all territory subject to the jurisdiction thereof for beverage purposes is hereby prohibited."

A. This amendment was adopted after a long "temperance" campaign that began prior to the Civil War.

   1. By 1900, _5_ states had adopted statewide prohibition.

   2. By 1916, _9_ states had adopted statewide prohibition.

   3. In 1917, the Lever Act was passed as a wartime food-control measure,

and alcoholic beverages were outlawed as a _waste_ of resources for the duration of World War I.

4. In 1917, Congress adopted Prohibition as an amendment to the Constitution. It was rapidly approved by enough state legislatures to make it part of the Constitution by January 29, 1919. Eventually, it was adopted by all but _____2_____ states.

B. The federal enforcement machinery was provided by Congress in the Volstead Act, but it ran into immediate resistance.

1. It might have worked if the prohibition had just been against hard liquor, but it included the _lighter_ alcoholic beverages such as beer and wine. Both of these are consumed by certain American ethnic groups as part of their meals. These people promptly began making their own home brew and wine.

2. The _scarcity_ of liquor created a certain amount of social status for those who could get it. Bootlegging and "speakeasies" became part of the American lifestyle in many areas.

3. The rapid increase in demand for bootleg liquor forced _prices_ sky-high, and this immediately attracted the gangster element.

4. By 1932 rum-running, racketeering, and the criminal violence associated with liquor made Prohibition very unpopular. The _21st_ Amendment was adopted in 1933 repealing Prohibition.

XIX ### *The Nineteenth Amendment*
(August 18, 1920)

The "women's suffrage amendment" reads: "The right of citizens of the United States to vote shall not be denied or abridged ... on account of sex."

A. The campaign for women's suffrage extended over nearly a century.

1. Wyoming Territory gave women the right to vote in _1869_.
2. Utah and Idaho gave women the right to vote in _1870_.
3. By 1900, _____4_____ states had given women the right to vote.
4. By 1916, _____11_____ states had given women the right to vote.
5. During World War I (September 1918), President Woodrow Wilson asked Congress to pass the women's suffrage amendment.

    a. The major argument against women's suffrage was the fact that men had been voting for the whole _family_.

    b. An important argument that finally won approval was the idea that giving women the vote might "clean up _politics_."

    c. The Nineteenth Amendment went into effect August 26, _1920_.

B. It was thought that the number of women participating in the voting process might _equal_ that of the men; however, the voting turnout of women is still considerably below that of men.

The Twentieth Amendment

(January 23, 1933)

The Twentieth Amendment is sometimes referred to as the "lame duck amendment." It has an interesting history:

A. Following ratification of the Constitution by the required number of states, the new government officially began operation on March 4, ___1789___, which was an odd-numbered year. Therefore, the terms of newly elected Senators and Representatives always began and ended on March 4.

B. Since Article I, Section 4, Clause 2 of the Constitution provided that sessions of Congress were to begin on the first Monday in December each year, Congressmen who were defeated in the November elections (always in ___even___-numbered years) were required to attend the next session until their terms expired the following March 4. Referred to as "lame ducks," they continued to represent people who had refused to reelect them.

C. Those Congressmen who had *won* the November elections were not entitled to take office until their predecessors' terms had expired. Therefore, since the next Congress would not assemble in a regular session until the December following March 4, they were not able to take office for more than ___13___ months after the election was held!

D. The Twentieth Amendment solved this serious problem by providing that the terms of Senators and Representatives shall begin and end at noon on the ___third___ day of January following the elections. Therefore, Congressmen are now able to take office some ___2___ months after they are elected instead of 13 months, as was once the case.

E. The amendment also specifies that the terms of the President and Vice President shall begin and end at noon on the ___twentieth___ day of January following the elections. Therefore, Congress has more than two weeks to assemble, organize, and count the electoral votes before the incoming President takes office. Previously, there had been a three-month delay before a new administration could begin operation.

XX

The Twenty-First Amendment

(December 5, 1933)

This amendment repealed the ___Eighteenth___ Amendment, and thereby ended Prohibition in the United States.

A. It should be noted that this amendment did not legalize intoxicating beverages. It simply turned the problem back to the ___States___.

B. Furthermore, Section 2 of this amendment prohibited the interstate transportation of alcoholic beverages into a state where it was a violation of the laws of that state.

XXII

F.D.R.

The Twenty-Second Amendment

(February 27, 1951)

This amendment limits the President of the United States to ___2___ terms.

A. The Founders were not certain how many terms a President should serve. Washington voted against a ___Single___ term in the Constitutional Convention, but he himself refused to serve more than two terms after being elected President.

B. Franklin D. Roosevelt was the ___frist___ President to gain the approval of his party and run for more than two terms. He died on April 12, 1945, just a little over a month after commencing his ___fourth___ term.

C. In the 1946 election, the Republicans gained control of both the House and Senate. They passed the Twenty-Second Amendment in March ___1947___, and it was ratified and became operative on February 27, 1951.

XXIII

The Twenty-Third Amendment

(March 29, 1961)

This amendment, which provides for presidential electors from the District of Columbia, would undoubtedly have been considered highly ___objectionable___ to the Founding Fathers.

A. The very reason why they gave Congress exclusive jurisdiction over the area surrounding the national capitol was so that it would not be politicalized or become a storm center of ___violence___ as Philadelphia became while it served as the capital.

B. If the residents of the District of Columbia felt isolated from the election process, they could very easily have been allowed to vote with the people of ___Maryland___, since the District was formerly a part of that state.

C. The authors of this amendment seemed to be laying the foundation for eventually making the District of Columbia an independent ___state___.

The real intent of those promoting this amendment came out in 1978, when they began a campaign in Congress to pass an amendment giving the District of Columbia two Senators and one Congressman just like one of the states. The amendment died after seven years because so many states refused to ratify it. It had proposed to do something that completely nullified the original intent of the Founders as set forth in Article I, Section 8, Clause 17.

XXIV

The Twenty-Fourth Amendment

(January 23, 1964)

In many of the southern states, a poll tax (head tax) of two or three dollars was assessed against each adult to cover the ___cost___ of elections. Even though the tax was small, it discouraged voting by both poor

_____ blacks _____ and poor ___ whites ___.

Therefore, Congress passed the Twenty-Fourth Amendment, which provided that no person could be prohibited from voting because of failure to pay a tax.

The Twenty-Fifth Amendment
(February 10, 1967)

This amendment defines the procedures for filling vacancies in the offices of President and Vice President.

A. Section 1 of this amendment was unnecessary, since it merely repeated what the Constitution had already provided in Article II, Section 1, Clause 6. This simply states that if the President dies or is incapacitated, the Vice President shall take his place.

B. Section 2 states that if the office of Vice President becomes vacant, then:

1. The President is authorized to ___ nominate ___ a replacement.

2. The nominee is then confirmed by merely a ___ majority ___ of those present in the House and the Senate.

C. Section 3 allows the President to voluntarily relinquish his office to the Vice President if at any time he feels incapacitated. When he recovers, he can take over his office again and the Vice President ___ must ___ step down.

D. Section 4 provides that if the Vice President and a majority of the Cabinet (or a review board set up by Congress) decide that the President is incapacitated, the Vice President advises Congress that he is taking over as ___ acting ___ President.

1. Notice that the initiative for unseating the President is in the Vice President, backed by a mere ___ majority ___ of the Cabinet or such other review board as Congress may establish.

2. After the President has been ousted and the Vice President has assumed power, the President can advise the leaders of the House and the Senate that he is really ___ able ___ to discharge his duties.

3. The Vice President then has four days to respond. Meanwhile, the Vice President continues to serve as the ___ acting ___ President.

4. If the Vice President ___ still ___ thinks the President is incapacitated, he so advises the leaders of the House and the Senate and continues acting as President.

5. The House and the Senate then have ___ 21 ___ days to make a decision. If they do not happen to be in session, they have 48 hours to assemble.

6. After an appropriate inquiry, the House and Senate must decide whether the President is incapacitated or not. If ___ 2/3 ___ of the House and Senate agree that he is not able to discharge his duties, then the Vice President "shall continue . . . as acting President." If the vote is less than two-thirds, then the President is allowed to resume his office.

E. This amendment was pushed through Congress in 1965 and ratified in 1967. It is considered by some authorities to be poorly structured.

1. Consider what this kind of procedure might have done to _Abraham Lincoln_ during the Civil War when he often stood alone in making some of his most difficult decisions.

2. It is believed that this amendment tends to encourage the type of political maneuvering which gave the United States, for the first time in its history, an _unelected_ President and an _unelected_ Vice President (Gerald Ford and Nelson Rockefeller).

XXVI | *The Twenty-Sixth Amendment*
(July 1, 1971)

The Twenty-Sixth Amendment reads as follows: "The right of citizens of the United States, who are eighteen years of age or older, to vote shall not be denied or abridged by the United States or by any state on account of age."

A. Traditionally, the proper age for adulthood and the right to vote had been set at _21_.

B. This amendment was passed by Congress on March 23, 1971, and was ratified in July of the same year. No amendment was ever pushed through as _quickly_ as this one.

C. Opponents of this amendment were fearful that the sponsors were trying to develop a bloc vote of young people at an age when they are often susceptible to an emotional appeal and will engage in overt political activism. This did _not_ happen.

1. They did not vote as a _bloc_ group.

2. They were just as reluctant to get out and vote as their _parents_ have been.

3. The vote of 18-year-olds has _not_ changed the political spectrum any more than women's suffrage did. This is quite different than many had expected.

XXVII | *The Twenty-Seventh Amendment*
(May 7, 1992)

This amendment ensures that any law changing the _compensation_ for Senators and Representatives will not take effect until the next _election_.

Conclusion

This brings us to the conclusion of this brief study of the Constitution of the United States. It has been our purpose to:

1. Refresh our memories on the American heritage and the background of the Founding Fathers.

2. Rediscover the great strength of the Founders' original success formula for freedom, prosperity, and peace.

3. Gain a better understanding of how its principles could be utilized to solve major problems today.

Appendix: Memorizing the Preamble
with Hand Motions

The charm of the Preamble is in its use of forceful verbs to capture the idea of positive action to achieve each of its six objectives. It is often difficult to keep these verbs in order. The following recitation of the Preamble in sign language is offered for the purpose of facilitating the memorizing of this significant part of the Constitution:

We (both hands pointing to chest)

the people (arms outstretched, palms up)

of the United States (fingers of both hands interlocked),

in order to form (hands held as though molding something)

a more perfect union (fingers curled and interlocked),

establish (outstretched hands pressing down)

justice (turn hands over and simulate balancing of scales),

insure (cover left thumb with right hand as protection)

domestic tranquility (hands palm to palm against cheek simulating sleep),

provide (open hands extended as though offering something)

for the common defense (fists doubled in posture of defense),

promote the general (military salute)

welfare (hand over heart),

and secure (right hand grasping in air)

the blessings of liberty (right arm high in Statue of Liberty pose)

to ourselves (hand on chest)

and our posterity (lift right hand stairstep fashion to indicate different heights),

do ordain (laying on of hands)

and establish (outstretched hands pressing down)

this Constitution (simulate unrolling a scroll)

for the United States (fingers of both hands interlocked)

of America (arms outstretched simulating eagle in flight).

Answers to Study Guide Blanks

Lesson One
I. seas
key
II. mistakes
round
sphere
moonshine
III. failed
Arab
20
IV. west
27,750
eastward
V. 3,000
Japan
westward
VI. Hispaniola
Aztecs
Incas
Ruler's
French
VII. Montreal
New Orleans
80,000
3 million
People's
VIII. Anglo-Saxon
corrupted
Magna Charta
Parliament
freemen
Petition of Rights
Bill of Rights
IX. communism
Christian
Puritans
Hooker
written
X. Mission
destiny
Geographically
population
servants
XI. France
German
German

juries
Ohio Valley
Stamp
quartering
Massacre
cheaper
Tea Party
Intolerable
Lexington
Concord
George Washington
1,000

Lesson Two
Intro. petitions
95
450
traitors
subjects
I. Canada
4,000
disowned
govern
6
II. difficult
3
5
weaknesses
son
taxed
III. 5
Roman
Greek
history
representative
ancient principles
identical
British
IV. *Common Sense*
17
4
10
14
denied

7
11
V. 17
1
2
self-evident
nature
equal
inalienable
others
protected
consent
duty
60
lost
author
blood
treason
revived
VI. representative
identical
Anglo-Saxon
abolish
eagle
pyramid
He
New

Lesson Three
I. army
fleet
navy
Philadelphia
resigned
illness
evils
equality
freedom
inherited
2
slavery
civil
criminal

eldest
abolish
death
cruel
fourth
II. success
Constitution
anarchy
tyranny
middle
ruler
men
taxes
violence
misery
people
center
People's
Jefferson
freemen
morality
vote
money
leaders
laws
God
victim
war
law
peaceful
III. Black Sea
IV. Roman
Celts
Vikings
government
freemen
tithing man
village
hundred
earl
sheriff
consent
limited
victim
V. natural
gold
silver
abundant
cheap
production
free
supply
demand

profit
worthwhile
quantity
quality
prices
variety
interference
Illegal force
Fraud
Monopoly
Debauchery
vice
try
buy
sell
fail
first
natural

Lesson Four
Intro. month
I. independence
strong
weak
executive
judicial
tax
enforce
anarchy
50
Congress
II. frustrating
army
navy
Tory
France
lost
III. George Washington
states
British
King
IV. defeat
Americans
Americans
British
Americans
Americans
British
Americans
Draw
Americans
British

British
Draw
British
Americans
British
British
British
Americans
Americans
British
Americans

Lesson Five
Intro. frightening
unity
depression
quarreling
foreign
Mississippi River
troops
hostility
failure
I. miracle
Nothing
trade
5
II. 55
Rogue
81
John Adams
Thomas Jefferson
8
able
III. advantage
Madison
15
IV. Rhode Island
George Washington
James Madison
30
Whole
slavery
population
commerce
resolutions
amending
Congress
4
V. smaller
Hamilton
life
life

3
federal
none
Madison
crisis
60
representation
one
population
equal
Detail
11
Style
Morris
VI. center
vertical
horizontal
few
numerous
horizontal
center
VII. 41
Bill
Rights
wept

Lesson Six
I. New York
8
people
10
6
4
2
1
II. Union
justice
tranquility
defense
welfare
liberty
III. Congress
orders
administrative
executive
Senate
judicial
IV. 2
25
7
30,000
500,000

governor
expelled
V. 2
6
one-third
30
9
Vice President
Chief Justice
VI. districts
3
20
VII. elected
quorum
two-thirds
secret
one-fifth
3
VIII. treason
felony
slander
increased
IX. amendments
dies
10
two-thirds
pocket

Lesson Seven
I. tariffs
debts
states
defense
general welfare
limitation
grant
power
limited
Jefferson
Madison
1936
$600 billion
federal
excuse
haves
have-nots
authority
crime
equal
funds
matching

43
$44 billion
self-government
uniformly
Yes
Equal
II. credit
trust
debt
inflation
debt
trillion
inheritance
immoral
inflation
expansion
balance
cause
security
shrink
decreases
survive
higher
lower
strike
political
buy
economically
profit
black
corruption
III. cheap
inspection
embargo
flow
transportation
war
depression
indirectly
Interstate
disputes
Price
Federal
transportation
production
alcohol
IV. encouraged
citizens
1870
involuntary
voluntary
6

Lesson Eight
I. gold
silver
gold
silver
Reserve
silver
Reserve
foreigners
uniformity
fraud
II. counterfeiting
Secret Service
silk
III. speed
security
Yes
No
IV. lifetime
50
17
Yes
Yes
VI. state
VII. declare
authorization
rules
VIII. 2
IX. navy
X. rules
XI. militia
male
insurrections
invasion
laws
XII. uniform
officers
XIII. violence
Twenty-third
consent
forts
arsenals
dock-yards
buildings
XIV. necessary
proper
Sec. 9
I. 1808
$10
17

compromises
II. invasion
insurrection
III. attainder
trial
serious
severe
protection
IV. population
V. tax
duty
VI. preference
VII. appropriation
VIII. nobility
Sec. 10 Congress
I. treaty
Coin
gold
silver
title
nobility
II. Congress
treasury
peace
state
war

Lesson Nine
I. smaller
100
full
agricultural
housing
atomic
labor
relief
welfare
Medicare
Social Security
educating
health
environmental
40
energy
Regulating
radio
television
food
drugs
regional

amendment
State
expensive
efficiency
Congress
states
II. 1
3
several
educational
property
60
President
Yes
law
Yes
Civil Service
1
Yes
Four
No
House
Senate
governors
popular
electors
Two
Twelfth
No
Yes
Senators
Representatives
Yes
No
No
Monday
December
capital
natural
35
14
Twenty-fifth
$200,000
$50,000
$60,000
$25,000
execute
Constitution
1862
No

No
postpone
punished
No
offense
No
two-thirds
executive
act
Congress
A majority
heads
commission
necessary
No
Yes
No
White House
Yes
Yes
State
veto
80
impeachment
Treason
Bribery
High crimes
misdemeanors
No
Andrew Johnson
Richard Nixon

Lesson Ten
Article III
I. Constitution
laws
states
Eleventh
10,000
II. district
appeal
Supreme
foreign
states
200
special
III. jury
20
police
security

refused
killed
IV. limited
force
strictly
Congress
states
two-thirds
three-fourths
V. treason
political
family
17
war
aid
comfort
war
police
Korea
Vietnam
2
death
family
Article IV
I. faith
credit
proof
II. natural
acquired
hunting
fees
III. return
safe
IV. obsolete
V. Dividing
Combining
Creating
equal
equal
Sagebrush
VI. Congress
treaty
ratify
VII. republican
initiative
invasion
violence
Article V
I. all
Two-thirds

three-fourths
two-thirds
three-fourths
II. 1808
consent
Article VI
I. debts
$25 million
$79 million
honor
II. Constitution
Laws
Treaties
constitution
III. oath
Article VII
I. 9
compel

Lesson Eleven
I. no
establishment
schools
Creator
moral
treat
live
judged
government
mankind
principles
united
supports
believe
new
first
republican
no
abuses
slander
force
no
assemble
no
petition
II. governor
males
17
45
females

inalienable
50
150
200
register
confiscate
III. save
abuse
paying
refused
IV. happiness
secure
unreasonable
Yes
No
No
Yes
life
threat
evidence
crime
true
V. grand
testify
due
just
VI. public
jury
state
district
informed
accusers
witnesses
defense
VII. twenty
opinion
valid
facts
VIII. bail
fines
cruel
IX. unnecessary
limited
X. chains
authority
No
violated
internal
external

Lesson Twelve
XI. compelled
consent

XII. weaknesses
separate
majority
majority
3
majority
2
President
XIII. after
war
constitutional
Yes
No
No
No
XIV. citizens
process
void
XV. women
Nineteenth
XVI. history
direct
indirect
direct
rich
2
amendment
77
0
1913
liars
10
XVII. legislatures
cool
radical
ignored
1913
design
XVIII. 5
9
waste
2
lighter
scarcity
prices
Twenty-first
XIX. 1869
1870
4
11
family
politics
1920

equal
XX. 1789
even
13
third
2
twentieth
XXI. Eighteenth
states
XXII. 2
single
first
fourth
1947
XXIII. objectionable
violence
Maryland
state
XXIV. cost
blacks
whites
XXV. nominate
majority
must
acting
majority
able
acting
still
21
two-thirds
Abraham Lincoln
unelected
unelected
XXVI. 21
quickly
not
bloc
parents
not
XXVII. compensation
election